Communicating Skills

LEVEL 4

Third Edition

Dave Martin

NELSON

CONTENTS

UNIT	WORD SKILLS	LANGUAGE SKILLS		WRITING SKILLS			STUDY SKILLS
		Punctuation and Capitalization	Grammar and Usage	Sentence Construction	Paragraph Construction	Composition Construction	
1	1 Identifying Words: *Are You a Good Detective?* 1		4 Nouns Are Naming Words 4	2 What Is a Sentence? 2 3 Writing Complete Sentences 3			
2		7 Using Capital Letters: Part 1 7	6 Common and Proper Nouns 6	5 Run-on Sentences 5			8 Do You Know Your Alphabet? Part 1 8
3		9 Using Capital Letters: Part 2 9		10 Four Kinds of Sentences 10			11 Do You Know Your Alphabet? Part 2 12
4		13 Using Capital Letters: Part 3 14	14 Singular and Plural Nouns: Part 1 15		15 What Is a Paragraph? 16		12 Finding Words in the Dictionary 13
5			17 Singular and Plural Nouns: Part 2 18		18 Topic Sentences Show The Way 19 19 Editing Topic Sentences 20		16 Using the Guide Words 17
6	22 Learning About Syllables 24 23 Animal Words 25		20 Verbs Are Action Words 21		24 Paragraph Unity 26		21 Reading the Entry 22
REVIEW UNITS 1–6 *p. 27*							
7	29 Synonyms: Words with Similar Meanings 33	25 Using Commas with Dates 29	27 Helping Verbs 31	28 Subject and Predicate 32			26 Using the Pronunciation Key 30
8		30 Using Commas with Addresses 34	32 Verb Tense: Using Verbs to Tell Time 36	31 Working with Compounds 35			
9		35 Using Commas in Direct Address 39		34 Combining Subjects and Predicates 38	33 More Practice with Paragraphs 37		36 Finding the Right Meaning 40
10			39 Irregular Verbs: Part 1 44	37 Making Subjects and Predicates Agree 41	38 Putting Ideas in Order 42		
11	42 Be Careful with *Two, Too,* and *To* 47	40 Using Commas with a Series 45	41 Problems with *There Is* and *There Are* 46		43 Writing a Paragraph That Explains 48		44 Following Directions 50
12	45 Homonyms 51		47 Irregular Verbs: Part 2 *p. 54*		46 Explaining with Examples *pp. 52*		
REVIEW UNITS 7–12 *p. 55*							

ii | Communicating Skills 4

UNIT	WORD SKILLS	LANGUAGE SKILLS		WRITING SKILLS			STUDY SKILLS
		Punctuation and Capitalization	Grammar and Usage	Sentence Construction	Paragraph Construction	Composition Construction	
13	48 Antonyms Are Opposites 57		50 Irregular Verbs: Part 3 59	49 Choosing Verbs Carefully 58	51 Explaining with Reasons 60		
14	52 Making New Words with Prefixes 61 55 Antonym Puzzles 64	53 Quotation Marks Around Exact Words 62		54 Combining Simple Sentences 63			
15	59 Using Prefixes to Make Antonyms 68	56 Quotations at the End of the Sentence 65	57 Pronouns Replace Nouns 66	58 Pronouns Make Your Writing Smoother 67			
16		62 Quotation Marks with Questions and Exclamations 72	60 Making Pronouns Agree 69			61 Writing a Friendly Letter 70	
17		63 Divided Quotations 73	65 Using Pronouns Correctly: Part 1 75	64 Changing Sentence Patterns 74		66 Writing Postcards 76	
18	70 Working with Suffixes 80		68 Using Pronouns Correctly: Parts 2 78 69 Using Pronouns Correctly: Part 3 79	67 New Ways to Begin 77			
REVIEW UNITS 13–18 *p. 81*							
19	74 Homonym Crossword 87 75 Confusing Pairs of Words 88	73 Punctuating Divided Questions 86	72 Using Pronouns Correctly: Part 4 84	71 More Practice with Combining Sentences 83			
20						76 The Time Order of a Story 89 77 Understanding Plot 90 78 Writing a Story 92	
21			81 Using Adjectives to Describe 96	82 Building Interesting Sentences with Adjectives 97		80 Writing Conversations 94 83 More Practice with Stories 98	79 Using a Thesaurus 93
22	85 Onomatopoeia: The Sound Is the Meaning 100			84 Using Adjectives to Join Sentences 99	86 Using Picture-Making Adjectives 102		

UNIT	WORD SKILLS	LANGUAGE SKILLS		WRITING SKILLS			STUDY SKILLS
		Punctuation and Capitalization	Grammar and Usage	Sentence Construction	Paragraph Construction	Composition Construction	
23			87 Adverbs Tell How, Where, and When *103*	89 Adverbs Make the Meaning Clear *106*	88 Writing Exciting Descriptions *104*		
24		90 Apostrophes with Contractions *107*	92 Adverbs: The *–ly* Clue *110*			91 Writing a Two-Paragraph Report *108*	
REVIEW UNITS 19–24 *p. 111*							
25		93 Apostrophes Show Ownership *113*	95 Adverbs Move Easily *116*		94 Persuasive Writing: Convince Me *114*		
26	96 Understanding Abbreviations *117*		97 Using Adjectives to Compare *118*	98 Adding Interest by Expanding Sentences *120*			
27	99 Explaining with Similes *121*		102 *It's* or *Its?* *124*	100 Linking Ideas with Compound Sentences *122*		101 More Practice Writing Stories *123*	
28	105 More Practice with Synonyms *127* 106 Synonym Word Search *128*	103 Apostrophes with Pronouns and Contractions *125*		104 Joining Sentences with *and, but,* and *or* *126*			
29	107 Antonym Crossword *129* 108 Learning About *Good* and *Well* *130*		109 *There, Their,* and *They're* *131*	110 More Practice with Combining Sentences *132*		111 More Practice with Sentence Variety *134*	
REVIEW UNITS 25–29 *p. 135*							
	Mini-Thesaurus *137*						Index *140*

EXERCISE 1 (Word Skills)
Identifying Words: Are You a Good Detective?

All English words are made from just 26 letters arranged in many different ways. Sometimes words have other words inside them. Sometimes words can be made into different words.

A. Sherlock Holmes was a storybook detective. He was an excellent detective because he knew where to look for clues. Once he found the clues he put them together to solve the mystery. Are you a good a detective? How many words can you make from the letters in the name "Sherlock Holmes"? You should be able to find at least fifteen.

_____

_____

_____

_____

B. Each of these scrambled words is the name of a vegetable. The answers are in the box below. You will not need to use all the words in the box.

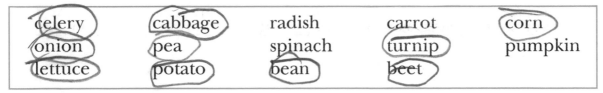

celery	cabbage	radish	carrot	corn
onion	pea	spinach	turnip	pumpkin
lettuce	potato	bean	beet	

EXAMPLE: ronc <u>corn</u>

1. eabn ___bean___
2. epa ___pea___
3. nnoio ___onion___
4. toapot ___potato___
5. telecut ___lettuce___

6. rcotar ___carrot___
7. eteb ___beet___
8. bbacega ___cabbage___
9. nruipt ___Turnip___
10. lecyre ___celery___

EXERCISE 2 (Sentence Construction)

What Is a Sentence?

A **sentence** is a group of words that makes sense by itself. A sentence always starts with a capital letter.

EXAMPLE: *Christopher built a model of the space station.*

Make sentences from each group of words.

1. shook head her Rachel.

   Rachel shook her head

2. sat quickly down Pardeep.

   Pardeep sat down quickly

3. hamster four our babies has.

   our Hamster has four babies

4. Mr. barked at Belmondo yesterday dog the.

   the dog barked at Mr. Belmondo

5. move turtles can than cats faster.

   cat move faster than turtles

6. frightened bed the under the hid mouse.

   the frightened mouse hid under the bed.

7. canoe the Ron water pushed Sandy into the and.

   Ron and sandy pushed the canoe into the water

EXERCISE 3 (Sentence Construction)

Writing Complete Sentences

Sometimes people write sentences that are incomplete. An **incomplete sentence** does not make sense by itself. Some words are missing.

EXAMPLE: *When Carmen opened the door*

What happened when Carmen opened the door? We do not know. Part of the sentence has been left out. Here are two ways to make the sentence complete:

EXAMPLE: *When Carmen opened the door, she saw a huge dragon.*
When Carmen opened the door, somebody laughed.

Add words to make each group of words into a complete sentence.

1. At midnight Adam _ate a big red apple._

2. Although the snow was deep _we still made a snowman_

3. Yesterday Yee-Ting and her sister _built a tree fort_

4. All at once Chris _ate a big mac and cheese bowl_

5. When you finish your lunch _you get to play nintendo_

6. Five minutes later the huge dinosaur _ate throug chickens_

7. On the way to school this morning _I saw a fat chipmunk_

EXERCISE 4 (Grammar and Usage)
Nouns Are Naming Words

Words that name people, animals, places, or things are called **nouns**.

EXAMPLE: people: her **aunt**, **Randy**, **Mrs. Wong**, the **dentist**
animals: the **spider**, a huge **snake**, two **starfish**, a white **kangaroo**
places: the **drugstore**, **North America**, my **bedroom**, **Calgary**
things: a **ruler**, a red **car**, the bright **star**, those **shoes**

A. Circle the nouns in these sentences. The number in parentheses tells you how many nouns are in each sentence.

1. Kelly and my sister found a wallet in the gymnasium. (4)

2. The kitten chased the yellow balloon across the lawn. (3)

3. The hungry giant swallowed seven hamburgers, several cakes, and a lemon pie. (4)

4. Maria put the lawnmower in the garage. (3)

5. Eagles usually build their nests in tall trees or on high cliffs. (4)

6. The cat carried the mouse up the stairs and into the kitchen. (4)

B. Write a noun to name each of the following:

EXAMPLE: a person who steals <u>robber</u>

1. a person who takes care of your teeth _____

2. the first meal of the day _____

3. the red liquid in your body _____

4. the place where a train stops _____

5. the part of your face you smell with _____

6. a funny person in a circus _____

Run-on Sentences

A **run-on sentence** is two or more complete sentences written as if they were one sentence.

> *EXAMPLE: Flamingos are beautiful water birds their necks and legs are very long often, flamingos rest by standing on one leg.*

This run-on sentence tells us three facts about flamingos. Each fact should be in a sentence of its own.

> *EXAMPLE: Flamingos are beautiful water birds. Their necks and legs are very long. Often, flamingos rest by standing on one leg.*

Read the following paragraph carefully. How many sentences can you find? Rewrite the paragraph. Start each sentence with a capital letter. Each sentence should end with a period.

there are about six million flamingos in the world more than half of them live in Africa flamingos are also found in Europe, Asia, South America, and the West Indies these birds usually live together in huge flocks flamingos spend most of their time near lakes and marshes

_____

_____

_____

_____

_____

_____

_____

EXERCISE 6 (Grammar and Usage)
Common and Proper Nouns

Nouns that name a *particular* person, a *particular* place, or a *particular* thing are called **proper nouns**. *Particular* means "special" or "belonging to one person or thing."

> EXAMPLE: The **woman** drove down the **street** in her new **car**.
> **Aunt Sharon** drove down **Oak Street** in her new **Mustang**.

In the second sentence, the noun "Aunt Sharon" is the name of one particular person. "Oak Street" is the name of one street. "Mustang" is the name of one kind of car. Special names like "Aunt Sharon," "Oak Street," and "Mustang" are proper nouns. Often, proper nouns contain more than one word. They always begin with a capital letter.

The nouns in the first sentence do not name a special person, place, or thing. These nouns are called **common nouns**. Common nouns begin with capitals only when they start a sentence.

A. Write a proper noun for each of these common nouns.

EXAMPLE: planet _Mars_

1. boy _Ethan_
2. river _Great Lawerence River_
3. store _Shoppers store_
4. month _March_
5. school _Crescent_
6. province _Ontario_

B. Rewrite the following sentences, replacing the common nouns with proper nouns.

EXAMPLE: Every morning my neighbour takes her dog for a walk around the lake.

Every morning Mrs. Feng takes Rusty for a walk around Burnaby Lake.

1. The principal said that the school would be closed for a holiday.

   The headmaster Mr. Felon said that crescent would be closed to a holiday

2. The car rolled down the street and crashed into a store.

   Bob's car rolled down main street and crashed into Ethan's cow store

EXERCISE 7 (Punctuation and Capitalization)
Using Capital Letters: Part 1

Each of the following kinds of proper nouns must start with a **capital**, or **upper-case**, letter.

The name of a person or an animal

EXAMPLE: Selina, Tommy, J.K. Rowling, Hedwig, Fluffy

The title of a person

EXAMPLE: Mrs. Jackson, Doctor Low, Professor Dumbledore, Reverend Longstaff

The names of the days of the week and the months of the year

EXAMPLE: Wednesday, Saturday, March, November

Do *not* use capitals with the names of the seasons (spring, summer, fall, and winter).

Rewrite these sentences. Use upper-case letters where they are needed.

1. doctor dundas saw andrea on tuesday.

   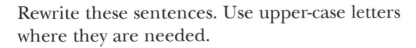

   Doctor Dundas saw Andrea on Tuesday

2. professor jang gave luke the test tubes last summer.

   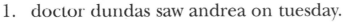
   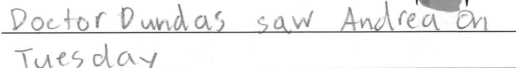

   Professor Jang gave Luke tubes last summer ✓

3. mike is looking after henry, mrs. hooper's pet turtle.

   Mike is looking after Henry, Mrs. Hoopers' pet turtle

4. last winter tina visited uncle fred.

   Las winter Tina visited Uncle Fred.

EXERCISE 8 (Study Skills)
Do You Know Your Alphabet? Part 1

Many things are listed in **alphabetical order**. To use a telephone book, for example, you must know the alphabet. Look at the fiction books in your school library. How are they organized on the shelves?

The words printed in heavy type, or boldface type, in a dictionary are called **entry words**. Entry words are always listed in alphabetical order. To find words in a dictionary quickly, you must know the alphabet well.

A. Write the words in each group in alphabetical order. Remember to look at the first letter in each word.

1. plastic, giant, short, club, mop

   club, giant, mop, plastic, short

2. milk, open, lucky, post, next

   lucky, milk, next, open, post

B. Sometimes all the words in a group begin with the same letter. Then you must look at the *second* letter in each word to put them in alphabetical order.

1. remind, roller, rabbit, rule, right

   rabbit, remind, right, roller, rule

2. skid, smoke, shirt, snap, sign, slap

   shirt, sign, skid, slap, smoke, snap

3. gift, garden, goat, grape, geese, glue

   garden, geese, gift, glue, goat, grape

4. wrong, with, worry, wet, white, wax

   wax, wet, white, with, worry, wrong

Using Capital Letters: Part 2

Here are some more proper nouns that must start with capital letters.

The names of holidays

EXAMPLE: Labour Day, Diwali, Valentine's Day, Hanukkah, Chinese New Year

The names of streets, towns, and cities

EXAMPLE: Highfield Avenue, Porter Street, Glenwood, Sudbury, Calgary

The names of rivers, lakes, oceans, mountains, provinces, countries, and continents

EXAMPLE: Red River, Lake Superior, Pacific Ocean, Rocky Mountains, New Brunswick, Canada, North America

UNIT 3

In the following sentences underline each proper noun. Cross out each small, or lower-case, letter that should be capitalized. Then write the upper-case letter above it.

EXAMPLE: last july we visited mount edith cavell in jasper national park.

1. the nelson river flows from lake winnipeg to hudson bay.

2. on new year's day, uncle clifford flew to edmonton.

3. mr. korzen now lives in toronto at 519 pine street.

4. last summer allison and nina climbed copper mountain.

5. mother's day is always the second sunday in may.

6. anita arrived in victoria on canada day.

7. saint john, the largest city in new brunswick, is on the bay of fundy.

8. during the winter alec often goes skiing on mount norquay in alberta.

EXERCISE 10 (Sentence Construction)
Four Kinds of Sentences

A sentence that tells something is called a **statement**. Use a period at the end of a statement.

    EXAMPLE: The orangutan stared through the leaves.

A sentence that needs an answer is a **question**. Use a question mark with a question.

    EXAMPLE: What does the orangutan eat?

A sentence that shows strong feeling is an **exclamation**. Use an exclamation mark with an exclamation.

    EXAMPLE: Wow, that orangutan is huge!

A sentence that gives a command is an **imperative**. Often it uses an exclamation mark.

    EXAMPLE: Watch out for the orangutan!

A. This story uses different kinds of sentences.

When Andy and Matt were halfway to the island, a strong wind began to blow. Both boys glanced anxiously at the black storm clouds.

"Do you think we'll reach shore before the rain starts?" asked Andy.

Suddenly a flash of lightning lit the sky. A crash of thunder rumbled through the hills. The wind whipped the water into waves.

"Paddle faster!" yelled Matt. "The canoe is starting to fill with water!"

"We'll never make it," gasped Andy.

Copy one of each kind of sentence from the story.

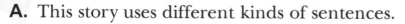

_____

_____

_____

_____

_____

Four Kinds of Sentences (continued)

B. Now write your own ending for the story about Andy and Matt. Before you start writing, take time to plan what you want to say.

What problems do the two boys have to solve?

_____

_____

_____

How can they solve these problems?

_____

_____

_____

Imagine that the wind gets stronger and the waves get even higher. What finally happens to the two boys?

_____

_____

Write an exciting ending for this story. Make sure to use the four kinds of sentences.

_____

_____

_____

_____

_____

_____

_____

Do You Know Your Alphabet? Part 2

You have already learned that putting words into alphabetical order means looking at the second letter of each word as well as the first one. Sometimes you have to look at even more letters to find the correct alphabetical order.

A. Write the following words in alphabetical order. You will need to look at the third letter in each word.

hawk, hair, hatch, hammer, habit, hay, hard, half, handcuff, happy

1. habit
2. hair
3. half
4. Hammer
5. handcuff

6. Happy
7. Hand
8. hatch
9. hawk
10. hay

B. For these words you may need to look at the fourth or even the fifth letter.

buckle, bunk, bulldozer, buggy, buffalo, bubble, bump, bug, bull, bucket

1. bubble
2. bucket
3. buckle
4. buffalo
5. buggy

6. buggy
7. bull
8. bulldozer
9. bump
10. bunk

Finding Words in the Dictionary

Suppose someone gave you a *catamaran* for your birthday. Would you eat it, fly it, or sail it? If you broke your *fibula*, would the doctor put a cast on your arm, your finger, or your leg? Would you expect to find a *carp* in a tree, a pond, or a corral? If you met a *gaucho*, would you be in Australia, South America, or Newfoundland? How do you pronounce *crochet* and *suede*?

The best place to find answers to questions such as these is in your dictionary. You will be able to find a word faster if you know where to look. Try to open the dictionary as close as possible to the word you want. Think of the dictionary as divided into four parts.

First Part	Second Part	Third Part	Fourth Part
A to D	E to L	M to R	S to Z

UNIT 4

In which part of the dictionary would you find each of these words?

EXAMPLE: motorboat <u>third</u>

1. berry _____

2. needle _____

3. velvet _____

4. jellybean _____

5. quail _____

6. thumbtack _____

7. globe _____

8. coconut _____

9. fluffy _____

10. wallet _____

11. dizzy _____

12. parsnip _____

13. arrow _____

14. kiwi _____

15. yawn _____

16. octopus _____

Using Capital Letters: Part 3

Here is another group of proper nouns that need capital letters.

The names of languages and nationalities

EXAMPLE: Spanish, Polish, English, Canadian, American, Chinese

The names of schools, buildings, bridges, and parks

EXAMPLE: Henderson School, Benton Hotel, Landmark Bridge, Maple Grove Park

The names of clubs, organizations, and businesses

EXAMPLE: Lions Club, Toronto Maple Leafs, Westwind Motel

The titles of books and movies

EXAMPLE: Star Wars, The Lion King

In the following sentences underline each proper noun. Then cross out each lower-case letter that should be capitalized. Write the upper-case letter above it.

EXAMPLE: there are many chinese restaurants on pender street in vancouver.

1. jasper national park, near edmonton, alberta, is one of the largest parks in north america.

2. when you are in toronto, be sure to visit the hockey hall of fame on yonge street.

3. on tuesday we had lunch at summerville beach park near liverpool, nova scotia.

4. in january 2003, the canadian figure skating championships took place in saskatoon, saskatchewan.

5. more than one third of the people in new brunswick speak french.

EXERCISE 14 (Grammar and Usage)
Singular and Plural Nouns: Part 1

A **singular** noun names *only one* person or thing.

  EXAMPLE: The **dog** chased the **cat** up the **tree**.

A **plural** noun names *more than one* person or thing.

  EXAMPLE: The **dogs** chased the **cats** up the **trees**.

Singular nouns can be changed into plural nouns in several ways. Most singular nouns are made plural by adding -s.

  EXAMPLE: *insect – insects   crab – crabs   gate – gates   video – videos*

Nouns that end in *ss, x, z, ch,* or *sh* are made plural by adding -es.

  EXAMPLE: *class – classes   box – boxes   ranch – ranches   wish – wishes*

Make each of these singular nouns plural.

1. glass _glasses_
2. hammer _hammers_
3. fox _foxes_
4. eyelash _eyelashes_
5. duck _ducks_
6. banana _bananas_
7. sandwich _sandwichs_
8. whale _whales_
9. princess _princesses_
10. needle _needles_
11. patch _patches_
12. grasshopper _grasshoppers_
13. cross _crosses_

14. dish _dishes_
15. match _matches_
16. cabin _cabins_
17. toothbrush _toothbrushes_
18. mailbox _mailboxes_
19. pirate _pirates_
20. branch _branches_

What Is a Paragraph?

A **paragraph** is a group of sentences that are about the same subject. This subject is called the **main idea** of the paragraph. Some paragraphs have many sentences. Others have only a few. In a well-written paragraph, however, all the sentences will be about one main idea.

   The first sentence of a paragraph always starts on a new line. The first word is indented, or moved over, like the first word in this paragraph. Sometimes a paragraph is not indented if it is the first paragraph of a composition or if there is only one paragraph.

All the following sentences are about the great horned owl. Read the sentences carefully. Do you think they all belong in one paragraph? Why?

1. The great horned owl likes to eat mammals but will also eat birds.
2. A full-grown adult owl is about twice as big as a large crow.
3. The mother owl lays two or three round, white eggs.
4. Rabbits are this owl's favourite food.
5. These birds are found all over North America.
6. The female sits on the eggs for about four weeks.
7. It also eats squirrels, mice, cats, water birds, chickens, and smaller owls.
8. These owls lay their eggs in the old nests of hawks, crows, and eagles.
9. On its head grow two feathered tufts that are called "horns."
10. Its enormous yellow eyes are surrounded by a ring of feathers.

Three of these sentences should be in a paragraph that tells what the owl looks like. Three of them belong in a paragraph that tells what the owl eats. Three of the sentences explain how the bird nests. Write the numbers of the sentences that belong beside each of these main ideas. One of the sentences does not belong with any of these ideas. Draw a line through this sentence.

1. What the owl looks like _____

2. What the owl eats _____

3. How the owl nests _____

Now, write the three paragraphs in your notebook.

EXERCISE 16 (Study Skills)
Using the Guide Words

At the top of each page in a dictionary are two words in boldface type. These words are called **guide words**. The guide word on the left is the *first* word on the page. The guide word on the right is the *last* word on the page. When you look up a word in a dictionary, these guide words tell you quickly which way to turn to find the word you want.

A. Find each of the following words in your dictionary. Write the guide words that are on the page where you find each word. Then list two more words from the same page. Be sure you know the meaning of the words you choose.

	Guide Words	Two More Words
1. parsnip	_____	_____
2. chess	_____	_____
3. worm	_____	_____
4. shingle	_____	_____

UNIT
5

B. Here are the guide words for four pages in a dictionary. On which page would each of the following words be found? Write the correct page number beside each word.

358 narrow • nearly   359 neat • nervous   360 nest • nibble   361 nice • nobody

EXAMPLE: needle 359

1. neck	_____	5. nine	_____	9. no	_____
2. newsprint	_____	6. necessary	_____	10. never	_____
3. natural	_____	7. nip	_____	11. nasty	_____
4. need	_____	8. naughty	_____	12. new	_____

EXERCISE 17 (Grammar and Usage)
Singular and Plural Nouns: Part 2

Making the plural form of nouns that end in *y* is easy. Just remember these rules.

1. If a vowel comes before the *y*, simply add -*s*.

EXAMPLE: *turkey – turkeys   tray – trays   boy – boys*

2. If a consonant comes before the *y*, change *y* to *i* and add -*es*.

EXAMPLE: *puppy – puppies   pony – ponies   story – stories*

A few nouns change their spelling when they become plural.

EXAMPLE: *foot – feet   ox – oxen   woman – women*

Some nouns have the same form in the singular and the plural.

EXAMPLE: *sheep – sheep   buffalo – buffalo   aircraft – aircraft*

In the blank write the plural form of each of these singular nouns.

1. lady _ladies_
2. mouse _mice_
3. candy _candies_
4. valley _valleys_
5. child _children_
6. holiday _holidays_
7. hobby _hobbies_
8. highway _highways_
9. poppy _poppies_
10. journey _journeys_
11. trout _trout_
12. penny _pennies_
13. birthday _birthdays_

14. man _men_
15. jockey _jockies_
16. cherry _cherries_
17. country _countries_
18. moose _moose_
19. toy _toys_
20. galaxy _galaxies_
21. fly _flies_
22. city _cities_
23. bay _bayes_
24. cry _cries_
25. salmon _salmon_
26. ferry _ferries_

Topic Sentences Show the Way

Writers use key sentences called **topic sentences** to tell the reader what a paragraph is about. Often the topic sentence is the first sentence in the paragraph.

A. Here is the beginning of a story by Roger Aske. The topic sentence is printed in slanted letters called italics.

I shall never forget the wind that day. It didn't just huff and puff in angry gusts up the street and through the trees. It growled and roared, carrying bushes and buckets and sheets of plywood from the new house at the bottom of the hill in frantic, tumbling flight. The trees didn't just bend and cry like they usually do. They seemed to crouch and lower their heads under the fierce lash of the wind. Some of them were split and broken where they fell across the driveways and onto the grass.

The topic sentence tells us that the paragraph will be about an unusual wind. List two things that happened that show that the wind was very powerful.

1. _____

2. _____

B. Here is a paragraph that does not have a topic sentence. Read the paragraph carefully to find the main idea.

First I arrived twenty minutes late for school. Then I discovered that I had left my science project at home. While playing soccer at noon, I tripped and skinned my knee. On the way home it suddenly started to rain.

Circle the statement that best tells the main idea of the paragraph.

How I got wet   A bad day at school   Why I do not like school

Now write an interesting topic sentence for the paragraph.

_____

EXERCISE 19 (Paragraph Construction)
Editing Topic Sentences

Making changes to improve your writing is called **editing**. Editing involves changing both *what* you said and *how* you said it.

Let's begin by learning how to edit topic sentences. A good topic sentence must tell the reader what the paragraph will be about. It must also be interesting and catch the reader's attention. Here is a topic sentence that needs improving.

EXAMPLE: *I am going to tell you about mountain biking.*

"Mountain biking" is too large a topic for one paragraph. Whole books have been written about mountain biking. Be sure that your topic sentence talks about only one part of your subject.

EXAMPLE: *Experts recommend that all mountain bikers wear safety helmets.*

Another way to improve a topic sentence is to use exact words and details. The following topic sentence is not exact. It is not clear what the paragraph will be about.

Not all bikes are the same.

Which words in the following sentence make the writer's ideas more exact?

Mountain bikes are made with strong, lightweight frames.

Each of these sentences is too general to be a good topic sentence. Edit each sentence. Add exact words and details. Be sure to tell the reader clearly what the paragraph will be about.

1. I like to play many sports.

   _____

2. I want to tell you about my pet.

   _____

3. Watching television is interesting.

   _____

4. We had a perfect vacation.

   _____

EXERCISE 20 (Grammar and Usage)
Verbs Are Action Words

Nouns are words that name people, animals, places, and things. **Verbs** tell what the nouns are doing. Often they are action words such as *eat, hit, run,* and *jump.*

EXAMPLE: *The dog* **chased** *the chickens across the barnyard.*

Sometimes verbs tell what is happening in someone's mind.

EXAMPLE: *All day Rachel* **thought** *about the party.*

Not all verbs show action. Some verbs help sentences state facts. These verbs tell us that something *is, was,* or *will be.*

EXAMPLE: *The Anne of Green Gables house is in Prince Edward Island.*

Some of the forms of the verb *be* are *is, was, were, am, are, be, been, shall be, will be, have been, has been,* and *had been.*

A. Think of an interesting verb that will go with each of these nouns. The first two have been done for you.

1. Parrots _____chatter_____ . 6. Students _____ .

2. Eyes _____blink_____ . 7. Frogs _____ .

3. Tigers _____ . 8. Soldiers _____ .

4. Dogs _____ . 9. Dinosaurs _____ .

5. Drums _____ . 10. Snakes _____ .

UNIT
6

B. Fill in the blanks in these sentences with an action word.

1. The huge wolf _____ slowly toward the small deer.

2. "Please get me out of here," _____ Andy.

3. Three of the fish _____ into the weeds.

4. All night the waves _____ against the rocks.

5. Carefully Farhaz _____ the strange box.

EXERCISE 21 (Study Skills)
Reading the Entry

To help you understand the meanings of words, dictionaries use definitions, examples, and pictures.

In the box at the right is the dictionary entry for the word *armadillo*. The entry tells you that an armadillo is "a small burrowing animal that has a very hard shell." This part of the entry is called the **definition**.

After the definition is an **example** printed in italics. The example shows you how the word is used in a sentence. Often it gives you added information about the word.

Many dictionaries also use **pictures** to make clear the meaning of a word. Be sure to read the **caption**, the words with the picture, as well.

ar•ma•dil•lo (ȧr′mə dil′ō) a small burrowing animal with armourlike coverings and strong claws. *pl.* **ar•ma•dil•los.** *Most armadillos live in South America but one kind lives as far north as the southern United States.*

A. Rewrite each of these sentences. Replace the word in boldface type with its definition. To make the sentence sound right, you may have to change some of the other words.

EXAMPLE: Our teacher read us a story about an **ogre**.

Our teacher read us a story about a giant that eats people.

1. My aunt plays the **bassoon.**

   _____

2. The stranger grabbed a **rapier**.

   _____

3. **Gibbons** live in the forests of India.

   _____

4. Does your mother have a **maroon** coat?

   _____

Reading the Entry (continued)

B. Try writing your own examples for these definitions. Remember that the example shows how the word is used in a sentence. Often it gives added information about the word.

EXAMPLE: **jade**   a hard stone used for jewellery or ornaments

_Jade is usually either green or white._____

1. **kelp** a large, tough, brown seaweed _____

   _____

2. **glider** an airplane without a
   motor _____

   _____

3. **chariot** a two-wheeled cart
   pulled by horses_____

   _____

   _____

4. **marsupial** an animal that carries its young in a pouch _____

   _____

5. **track** a mark left by anything that moves _____

   _____

6. **dinosaur** an extinct reptile of enormous size _____

   _____

7. **pepper** a seasoning with a hot taste _____

   _____

8. **sky** the space high above the Earth_____

   _____

EXERCISE 22 (Word Skills)
Learning About Syllables

A **syllable** is a word or part of a word that contains a vowel sound. A word has as many syllables as it has vowel sounds.

 EXAMPLE: bat   house   tree

Each of these words has only one vowel sound. They are one-syllable words. Notice that even though the word *house* has three vowels, it has only one vowel sound.

Some words have more than one syllable.

 EXAMPLE: es • cape   im • por • tant   au • to • mo • bile

In words of two or more syllables, one syllable is usually said with more force than the others. The amount of force or loudness that you give to a syllable is called **stress**. In a dictionary the stressed syllable is marked with a slanted line ('). This line is called a **stress mark** or **accent mark**.

 EXAMPLE: helmet (hel' mit)   inside (in sīd')   elastic (i las' tik)

Say each of the following words to yourself. Listen carefully for vowel sounds. Rewrite each word leaving a space between the syllables. Mark the syllable that is stressed with an accent mark. Use your dictionary to check your work.

EXAMPLE: unhappy _____un hap' ē_____

1. rabbit _____
2. behind _____
3. banjo _____
4. smoky _____
5. invent _____
6. tornado _____
7. plastic _____
8. admit _____

9. ostrich _____
10. repeat _____
11. remember _____
12. volcano _____
13. sandwich _____
14. rubbish _____
15. piano _____
16. magnet _____

EXERCISE 23 (Word Skills)
Animal Words

Writing stories about animals can be fun. Before you start, however, you need to research your animal and find the correct words to use. Baby animals often have special names.

> EXAMPLE: A young cow or bull is called a **calf** (kaf).
> A newborn swan is called a **cygnet** (sig nit).

The male and female of most animals have different names.

> EXAMPLE: A female deer is called a **doe** and a male is a **buck**.

A. Complete this chart with words from the list below. Use your dictionary if you are not sure about the answer. You will not use all the words.

boar	mare	buck	doe	ewe	nanny
billy	hen	sow	ram	stallion	rooster

Animal	Female	Male
horse		
goat		
chicken		
pig		
sheep		

B. Complete these sentences, using words from the box below. Use your dictionary if needed.

cub	pup	gosling	kid	kitten	calf	lamb	fawn

1. A young cat is a _____
2. A young bear is a _____
3. A young sheep is a _____
4. A young goat is a _____

5. A young dog is a _____
6. A young goose is a _____
7. A young deer is a _____
8. A young whale is a _____

Paragraph Unity

In Lesson 15 you learned that a paragraph tells about one main idea. Usually the topic sentence tells what the main idea is. The other sentences in the paragraph are called detail sentences. Their job is to give details or facts that help the reader to understand the main idea. When all the detail sentences talk about the main idea, we say that the paragraph has **unity**.

When you edit your work, be sure to check to make sure that all the sentences belong. After you read each sentence, ask yourself "What does this sentence tell me about the main idea?" If the sentence does not give more information about the main idea, it does not belong in the paragraph.

Here is a paragraph about an unusual group of kangaroos. Read the paragraph through once to discover what the main idea is.

Did you know that some kangaroos spend most of their lives in trees? Tree kangaroos live in the forests of northeastern Australia. My Uncle Charlie moved to Australia in 1981. Their front legs are long and strong. They have sharp powerful claws on their front feet. Another animal with powerful claws is the anteater. To keep them from slipping, the tree kangaroos' hind feet have rough pads. By using all four legs, they can quickly climb to the top of the tallest tree.

1. Underline the topic sentence in this paragraph.

2. What does the topic sentence say that the paragraph will be about?

_____

3. Now read each sentence carefully to see whether it talks about the main idea. Cross out the two sentences that do not belong in this paragraph.

REVIEW

A. Underline each proper noun. Then cross out each lower-case letter that should be capitalized. Write the capital letter above it.

1. on thanksgiving day we camped at rushing river provincial park.

2. my sister maya teaches french at westwind elementary school on nelson avenue.

3. the largest cities in saskatchewan are regina and saskatoon.

4. on wednesday we visited the canadian ski museum in ottawa.

5. canadian figure skaters jamie salé and david pelletier won gold medals in figure skating at the 2002 olympics in salt lake city.

B. Here are the guide words for four pages in a dictionary.

On which page would each of the following words be found? Write the correct page number beside each word.

1. drag _____

2. dock _____

3. dog _____

4. doorbell _____

5. double _____

6. dizzy _____

7. downhill _____

8. domino _____

9. donate _____

10. dragon _____

11. diving _____

12. dough _____

13. dose _____

14. division _____

15. dogwood _____

16. dozen _____

17. dot _____

18. draft _____

19. divide _____

20. dodo _____

21. dollar _____

Review (continued)

C. Make each of these singular nouns plural.

1. peach _____   7. candy _____

2. raspberry _____   8. hairbrush _____

3. deer _____   9. tooth _____

4. toy _____   10. ranch _____

5. goose _____   11. donkey _____

6. robin _____   12. fish _____

D. Read the following paragraph carefully. As you read, watch for run-on sentences and sentences that are incomplete.

(1) In the deserts of North Africa the most important tree is the date palm. (2) For thousands of years people have eaten the fruit of the date palm. (3) Because dates are half sugar. (4) They are nourishing. (5) The tree's buds are also eaten as a vegetable or in salad. (6) The seeds from the fruit can be roasted to make a drink like coffee sometimes the seeds are ground up for cattle feed. (7) A palm wine is made from the tree's sap. (8) The people of North Africa weave baskets from the large leaves the fibres of these leaves are used to make rope. (9) Even the trunk is valuable for fuel and building materials. (10) Because the date palm has so many uses. (11) The desert people say there is one for every day of the year.

1. Write the numbers of the two sentences that are incomplete.

   _____

2. Write the numbers of the two sentences that run together.

   _____

3. Rewrite one of the incomplete sentences to make it complete.

   _____

EXERCISE 25 (Punctuation and Capitalization)
Using Commas with Dates

Punctuation marks are important. Katrina Klassen is a police officer. One day a traffic light stopped working. Katrina stood in the middle of the street to direct traffic. She told the drivers what to do by using her hands and a whistle. By watching Katrina, they knew when to stop, go, or slow down.

When you write, you must use punctuation marks just as Katrina used her hands. If you want your reader to stop, use a **period**, a **question mark**, or an **exclamation mark**. When you want to signal a pause, use a **comma**.

One place to use commas is in dates. Use a comma between the day of the month and the year.

EXAMPLE: *The Canadian women's hockey team won the Olympic gold medal on February 21, 2002.*

If the date comes inside the sentence, a comma is also needed after the year.

EXAMPLE : *On February 21, 2002, the Canadian women's hockey team won the Olympic gold medal.*

A. Add commas where they are needed in these sentences.

1. My grandmother was born on April 5 1942.

2. On June 30 2002 they reached the top of Mount Frosty.

3. We found an old letter dated August 27 1887 in the trunk.

B. Answer these questions in complete sentences. In your answer include the day of the month and the year. Be sure to use commas correctly.

1. When were you born?

   _____

2. When will you be nineteen years old?

   _____

EXERCISE 26 (Study Skills)
Using the Pronunciation Key

A dictionary can help you know how to pronounce a word. The pronunciation is shown in parentheses right after the entry word. Sometimes the pronunciation looks the same as the spelling of the word.

EXAMPLE: *pal (pal)*   *drop (drop)*   *brush (brush)*

In English, however, many words are not pronounced exactly as they are spelled.

EXAMPLE: *boat (bōt)*   *high (hī)*   *place (plās)*   *caught (kot)*

To know how to say words like these, you must use your dictionary's **pronunciation key**. A pronunciation key tells you how to pronounce the vowels and consonants in a word. Usually a complete pronunciation key is printed in the front of the dictionary.

In the box below is a pronunciation key from a dictionary. Using this key, spell out each of the following words. The answers are in the box at the end of the exercise.

EXAMPLE: krēm _cream_

cat	stär	ēv'ən	ice	ōld	kup	rūl
āt	pet	is	pot	ȯr'inj	fu̇l	

1. sitē _____   5. krāzē _____

2. krī _____   6. chūz _____

3. kōm _____   7. sīklōn _____

4. kof _____   8. kofē _____

city	cough	crazy	choose	comb	cyclone	coffee	cry

Now write the words in alphabetical order.

_____

_____

EXERCISE 27 (Grammar and Usage)
Helping Verbs

Sometimes a verb is made of more than one word. The verb parts that come before the main verb are called **helping verbs**.

> EXAMPLE: The detective **had parked** her car in the lane.

Some sentences have two helping verbs before the main verb.

> EXAMPLE: Jasmine **should have won** the race.

Sometimes the helping verb and the main verb are separated by words that are not verbs.

> EXAMPLE: Loren **did** not **remember** his skates.

Here is a list of the most important helping verbs:

am	was	be	has	do	must	can	will	shall
is	were	been	have	does	may	could	would	should
are			had	did	might			

Circle each main verb. Underline the helping verbs.

EXAMPLE: Now the boys will (sing) a song.

1. Roxanne should finish before eight o'clock.

2. The thieves must have broken the window.

3. I could never jump that high.

4. By three o'clock the girls had walked six kilometres.

5. Nicole did not see the rattlesnake.

6. After school Ming and I will wash the car.

7. Roberto will probably come about noon.

8. My brother might have eaten the cake.

9. The bus should have arrived at ten o'clock.

10. Charlie did not close the window.

EXERCISE 28 (Sentence Construction)

Subject and Predicate

A sentence always has two parts. The first part tells who or what the sentence is about. This part is called the **subject**. The second part of the sentence is the **predicate**. It gives information about the subject. Often the predicate explains what the subject does.

Subject: Who or What is the Sentence About?	Predicate: What Do We Learn About the Subject?
Mount Logan	is the highest mountain in Canada.
Six of my sister's pet snakes	escaped last night.

A. Complete each of the following sentences with an interesting subject.

1. _____ scored the winning goal.

2. _____ tasted like rubber.

3. _____ ate the tall grass.

4. _____ filled our basement.

B. Complete each of the following sentences with an interesting predicate.

1. The angry mother skunk _____

    _____

2. The old house on Elm Street _____

    _____

3. Six enormous elephants _____

    _____

4. Several strange creatures from Mars _____

    _____

Synonyms: Words with Similar Meanings

Words that have the same or nearly the same meaning are called **synonyms**.

EXAMPLE: *little – small*   *big – large*   *old – ancient*

A. The words listed below mean *happy* or *sad*. If a word is a synonym for *happy*, write **H** in the blank. If the word is a synonym for *sad*, write **S** in the blank. Check those you are not sure of in the dictionary.

1. _H_ glad

2. _S_ miserable

3. _H_ joyful

4. _H_ delighted

5. _S_ discouraged

6. _S_ sorrowful

7. _H_ thrilled

8. _S_ unhappy

9. _S_ gloomy

10. _H_ jubilant

11. _S_ dejected

12. _H_ merry

B. Write a synonym for each of these words. Use your dictionary if necessary.

1. wonderful _amazing_

2. smart _Big brain_

3. scream _yell_

4. sad _unhappy_

5. begin _start_

6. cool _cold_

7. strange _sus_

8. thin _skiny_

9. dirty _filthy_

10. noisy _loud_

11. tiny _small_

12. strong _bold_

13. easy _simple_

14. rough _bumpy_

15. damp _wet_

16. close _near_

17. pretty _beautiful_

18. quick _fast_

UNIT
8

Exercise 30 (Punctuation and Capitalization)

Using Commas with Addresses

When an address is part of a sentence, use a comma to separate the city from the street.

EXAMPLE: *The parcel was mailed to 504 College Street, Peterborough.*

Commas must also be used to separate the province, state, and country from the rest of the sentence.

EXAMPLE: *My grandfather has lived in Oslo, Norway, all his life.*

Do not use a comma between the province and the postal code.

EXAMPLE: *Helen's new address is 240 Grafton Street, Charlottetown, Prince Edward Island C1A 1L5.*

A. Add commas where they are needed in these sentences.

1. Send this letter to Tony Bertolo 326 Dufferin Avenue London Ontario N6A 4L6.

2. A giant explosion in Halifax Nova Scotia on December 6 1917 damaged every building in the city.

3. Our relatives from Stockholm Sweden are here.

4. The bus trip from Vancouver British Columbia to Calgary Alberta took eighteen hours.

B. Answer the following questions in complete sentences. Be sure to add commas where they are needed.

1. What is your mailing address?

_____

_____

2. What is the name and address of your school?

_____

EXERCISE 31 (Sentence Construction)
Working with Compounds

Joining two words together makes a **compound word**.

EXAMPLE: *waterfall*   *sunburn*   *blackberry*

To make sentences more interesting, we sometimes join two or more nouns together to make a **compound subject**. Often the nouns are joined by the word *and*.

EXAMPLE: **Sailfish, dolphins,** and **barracudas** *swim very fast.*

When a subject has more than one verb, the sentence has a **compound predicate**.

EXAMPLE: *Antonio* **baked** *the bread,* **washed** *the dishes, and* **scrubbed** *the floor.*

In this sentence, the subject Antonio has three verbs: *baked, washed,* and *scrubbed*.

Each of these sentences has a compound subject or a compound predicate. Draw one line under each noun in the compound subjects. Draw two lines under each verb in the compound predicates.

1. The cat crept through the bushes and pounced on the mouse.

2. Hans, Lars, and Engel arrived from Austria yesterday.

3. The old car coughed, sputtered, lurched, and stopped.

4. Alicia raced across the sand and jumped into the water.

5. Saint John, Moncton, and Fredericton are important cities in New Brunswick.

6. Farzeen washed and polished the car on Sunday.

7. Amy and I went to a movie.

Verb Tense: Using Verbs to Tell Time

Verbs tell what is happening in a sentence. Verbs also tell us when something happened.

> *EXAMPLE: Louisa **plays** goalie for the Wildcats.*
> *Yesterday Louisa **played** goalie for the Wildcats.*

Plays and *played* are two forms of the same verb. The form *plays* tells us that the action is taking place now, or in the **present**. The form *played* shows that the action took place in the **past**. These different verb forms are called **tenses**.

Forming the past tense is easy if you remember these rules:

1. If the present tense ends in e, add -d.

   EXAMPLE: wave – waved   doze – dozed

2. If the present tense does not end in e, add -ed.

   EXAMPLE: look – looked   coat – coated

3. If the present tense ends in *y*, change the *y* to *i* and add -ed.

   EXAMPLE: worry – worried   carry – carried

4. If the present tense has only one vowel and ends in a single consonant, double the consonant before adding -ed.

   EXAMPLE: trap – trapped   sob – sobbed

Verbs that form the past tense by adding -d or -ed are called **regular verbs**.

Write the past tense of each of the following verbs. After each verb write the number of the rule you used to get the answer.

EXAMPLE: miss <u>missed 2</u>

1. try _____

2. drop _____

3. paint _____

4. smile _____

5. bat _____

6. score _____

7. fry _____

8. follow _____

9. hurry _____

10. walk _____

EXERCISE 33 (Paragraph Construction)
More Practice with Paragraphs

Remember that a paragraph has a topic sentence that states the main idea and that the other sentences in the paragraph must be about that main idea.

Suppose you went to the library and learned the following details about helicopters:

1. spray crops to kill insects and weeds

2. herd cattle and look for strays

3. called "whirlybirds" or "choppers"

4. help police spot traffic problems

5. rescue injured or trapped people

6. fly more slowly than airplanes

7. carry firefighters to forest fires

Two of these facts do not belong in a paragraph about the uses of helicopters. Cross them out. Now write a paragraph using the rest of the details. When you finish writing your paragraph, edit your work to make sure that the sentences do not all start in the same way. Use the following sentence as your topic sentence.

Helicopters are used for an amazing number of jobs.

_____

_____

_____

_____

_____

_____

UNIT
9

EXERCISE 34 (Sentence Construction)
Combining Subjects and Predicates

Sometimes two sentences have the same predicate.

> EXAMPLE: *Arlene painted the fence. Dominic painted the fence.*

These subjects may be combined, or joined together, with the word *and*.

> EXAMPLE: *Arlene and Dominic painted the fence.*

The new sentence has a compound subject. It has two nouns: *Arlene* and *Dominic*.

The following sentences both have the same noun as a subject.
My uncle scrubbed the floor. My uncle washed the windows.
Now let's combine the predicates.
My uncle scrubbed the floor and washed the windows.
The new sentence has a compound predicate. It contains two verbs: *scrubbed* and *washed*.

Combine each of the following pairs of sentences into one sentence. Your new sentence should have either a compound subject or a compound predicate. Underline the nouns in the compound subjects. Circle the verbs in the compound predicates.

1. Heidi lived in Ottawa. Rosanne lived in Ottawa.

   _____

   _____

2. The mountain biker raced down the hill. She skidded around the corner.

   _____

   _____

3. The sailors dove into the water. The sailors swam toward the shore.

   _____

   _____

EXERCISE 35 (Punctuation and Capitalization)
Using Commas in Direct Address

Punctuation marks can change the meaning of a sentence. How does the meaning of the following sentence change when the commas are left out?

EXAMPLE: We are going to eat, Randy, before we cross the river.
EXAMPLE: We are going to eat Randy before we cross the river.

When you **address** someone, you speak directly to him or her. Listen as you say each of these sentences softly to yourself.

Do not forget to lock the door, Ben.
Marisa, please open the window.

Notice how you pause just before the noun "Ben" and after the noun "Marisa." In written English, this pause is shown with a comma.

Sometimes the name of the person addressed comes in the middle of the sentence.

EXAMPLE: Are you sure, Sonya, that you do not want to come?

Notice that this sentence needs two commas.

In the following sentences circle the name of the person being addressed. Add commas where they are needed. Remember that commas are also used with dates and addresses.

1. Would you like raisin pie or chocolate cake Mary?

2. Your camcorder is in the top drawer of your desk Rob.

3. Do not forget Allison that Uncle Bill will be here on Monday February 22.

4. Do you remember what the doctor said Dad?

5. Tristan change the address to 6457 Maple Street Halifax Nova Scotia.

6. Can you come for supper on Friday October 9 Sandy?

7. Lauren please take the seat at the back.

UNIT 9

Finding the Right Meaning

Often a word has more than one meaning. In the box at the right, for example, is the dictionary entry for the word *coat*. Four different meanings of the word are listed.

Sometimes definitions are followed by an example printed in slanted letters called *italics*. These examples show how the word is used in a sentence. They also help to explain how one meaning is different from another.

> **coat** (kōt) **1** a piece of clothing with sleeves, worn over other clothes. **2** the fur or hair of an animal. **3** Sometimes, **coating**, a thin layer: *a coat of paint.* **4** cover with a thin layer: *to coat a floor with varnish. This pill is coated with sugar.* 1–3 *n.*, 4 *v.*

Look up each of the following words in italics in your dictionary. Read all the definitions carefully. Below each sentence, write the meaning that makes sense in that particular sentence.

EXAMPLE: Leave the tools in the *shed.*   <u>a building used for storage</u>

1. The monkey sat in the *fork* of the tree.

   _____

2. Your jacket is *right* where you left it.

   _____

3. About noon the horses stopped to drink from a *spring*.

   _____

4. The rancher rode a *bay* horse.

   _____

5. The huge rocket rose slowly from the *pad*.

   _____

6. Be here at three o'clock *sharp*.

   _____

EXERCISE 37 (Sentence Construction)
Making Subjects and Predicates Agree

Always check to make sure that your verb and its subject fit together. If the subject is singular, the verb must be singular too.

EXAMPLE: Sometimes my mother **walks** *to work.*

If the subject is plural, the verb must be plural.

EXAMPLE: Pat and Nancy **walk** *to school every day.*

When the subject and the verb fit together, we say that they **agree**. Usually a verb ending in *s* is singular and a noun ending in *s* is plural.

EXAMPLE: the rabbit jumps–the rabbits jump   a bell rings–the bells ring

A. In the following sentences circle the subject of each verb. Decide whether the subject is singular or plural. Then cross out the incorrect verb.

EXAMPLE: My (brother) (**like**, likes) to make chocolate cake.

1. The lawn (needs, need) cutting.

2. Those girls (lives, live) in Saskatoon.

3. My cousin (plays, play) the organ.

4. Our roof (leaks, leak).

5. Nick and Paulo (knows, know) the way.

B. Rewrite the following sentences. If the subject is singular, make it plural. If the subject is plural, make it singular. Be sure to make the subject and the verb agree.

1. The canary often sings at about three o'clock.

   _____

2. Our puppies sleep all afternoon.

   _____

EXERCISE 38 (Paragraph Construction)
Putting Ideas in Order

The word **order** means "to put things together according to a plan."

A. Each morning when you get up to go to school you probably do the same things in the same order. Here are some activities. On the line below the list, write the numbers of the activities in the order in which you do them.

1. Brush your teeth

2. Go to the kitchen for breakfast

3. Get out of bed

4. Find what you need for school

5. Get dressed

6. Wake up

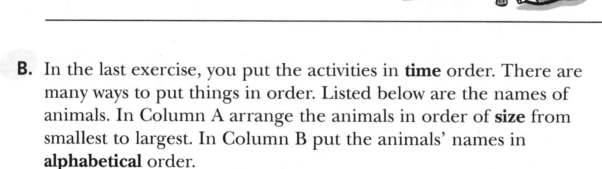

_____

B. In the last exercise, you put the activities in **time** order. There are many ways to put things in order. Listed below are the names of animals. In Column A arrange the animals in order of **size** from smallest to largest. In Column B put the animals' names in **alphabetical** order.

	Column A	Column B
1. gorilla	1. _____	1. _____
2. grasshopper	2. _____	2. _____
3. skunk	3. _____	3. _____
4. goat	4. _____	4. _____
5. rhinoceros	5. _____	5. _____
6. squirrel	6. _____	6. _____

Putting Ideas in Order (continued)

C. Now try arranging these groups of words in an order that makes
sense. Put 1 in the blank beside the step that should come first,
2 beside the second step and so on.

Giving a Dog a Bath

_____ Fill the tub with water.

_____ Put away the towel, soap, and tub.

_____ Rub the wet fur with soap.

_____ Get a towel, soap, and tub.

_____ Put the dog in the tub.

_____ Dry the dog.

_____ Rinse off the soap.

_____ Wet the dog's fur.

_____ Catch the dog.

Making a Cake

_____ Add some water.

_____ Pour the mixture into a pan.

_____ Bake for thirty minutes.

_____ Open the cake mix package.

_____ Taste the finished masterpiece.

_____ Put the cake in the oven.

_____ Turn the oven on.

_____ Pour the cake mix into a bowl.

_____ Ice the cake when it cools.

_____ Stir well.

UNIT
10

Irregular Verbs: Part 1

Regular verbs always need -*d* or -*ed* to make their past tense forms. A few verbs do not follow this pattern. They are called **irregular verbs**. These verbs change their forms in unusual ways. The form of the verb that is used after the helping verbs *has*, *have*, or *had* is called the **past participle**.

Present Tense	Past Tense	Past Participle
(Today I)	(Yesterday I)	(During the past week I)
see	saw	(have) seen
do	did	(have) done
run	ran	(have) run
begin	began	(have) begun
go	went	(have) gone
take	took	(have) taken
eat	ate	(have) eaten
beat	beat	(have) beaten

Complete each sentence with the correct form of the verb in parentheses. Use the past participle after all helping verbs.

EXAMPLE: The race __began__ (begin) at seven o'clock.

1. Have you _____ (see) my aunt's new sports car?

2. The well has _____ (run) dry.

3. On Monday the Edmonton Oilers _____ (beat) the Vancouver Canucks.

4. Has the bell _____ (go) already?

5. The puppy _____ (eat) all it could and then slept.

6. Have you _____ (take) enough to eat?

7. Ms. Wolanski _____ (do) it by herself.

8. The race _____ (begin) at seven o'clock.

9. Last Sunday Julie _____ (go) for a walk in the park.

Using Commas with a Series

Often we list a number of similar words in a series. This sentence has a series of nouns.

*EXAMPLE: People in New Brunswick catch **lobsters, salmon, sardines**, and **cod**.*

Sometimes the series is made up of groups of words.

*EXAMPLE: When we were in Toronto, we visited the **CN Tower**, the **Ontario Science Centre**, and the **Hockey Hall of Fame**.*

Notice that commas are used to separate the parts of a series. If you have a series of three items, you need two commas. If you have a series of four items, you need three commas, and so on.

A. In each of these sentences underline the word or group of words that is part of a series. Punctuate each sentence correctly.

1. Ingrid Erin and Mario play clarinets in the school band.

2. The hungry crocodile scrambled down the hill through the bushes and into the water.

3. The largest planets are Jupiter Saturn Uranus and Neptune.

4. The coyote has large ears long legs and a bushy tail.

5. Mr. Kalinsky put a dozen eggs a bottle of ketchup and five oranges in the refrigerator.

B. Fill each blank in these sentences with an interesting series of three or more items. Punctuate each sentence correctly.

1. As I walked along the beach I picked up _____

_____

2. In the old chest the pirates discovered _____

_____

EXERCISE 41 (Grammar and Usage)
Problems with *There is* and *There are*

Be careful with sentences that start with *here* or *there*. In these sentences the subject follows the verb.

> EXAMPLE: Here **are** the **books** that you wanted.
> There **is** a **parrot** in our cherry tree.

When you start a sentence with *here* or *there*, you must think ahead. Always ask yourself, "Will the subject be singular or plural?" Then choose the correct verb form.

A. In each of these sentences underline the noun that is the subject. Above the noun write **S** is the subject is singular. Write **P** if the subject is plural. Write the form of the verb that agrees with the subject in the blank at the right.

1. There (is, are) seventeen teachers in our school. _____

2. Here (is, are) your lost socks. _____

3. There (is not, are not) any cake left. _____

4. There (is, are) some pencils in the drawer. _____

5. Here (is, are) a map of Victoria. _____

B. Answer each of these questions in a complete sentence. Use *there is* or *there are* in your answer.

EXAMPLE: How many provinces are there in Canada?

There are ten provinces in Canada.

1. How many girls are there in your class?

_____

2. How many maple leaves are on the Canadian flag?

_____

Be Careful with *Two, Too,* and *To*

Students sometimes make mistakes with the words *two, too,* and *to*. The easiest word to remember is *two*. It means "one more than one."

*EXAMPLE: The **two** prairie dogs watched carefully for danger.*

The word *too* has three different meanings.

*EXAMPLE: Rhona is coming **too**. (**also**)*
*EXAMPLE: My sister ate **too** much. (**more than enough**)*
*EXAMPLE: Do not move **too** quickly. (**very**)*

To is used for all other meanings.

*EXAMPLE: Tie the dog **to** the tree.*

A. Fill in the blanks with *two, too,* or *to.*

1. It is _____ bad that the _____ boys could not go _____.

2. Take the _____ letters _____ the principal.

3. The iron is still _____ hot _____ touch.

4. Zachary likes _____ ski _____

5. I am _____ tired _____ play any more.

6. Emma took _____ books back _____ the library.

7. The ball bounced _____ high _____ catch.

8. Are _____ boxes _____ heavy for you _____ carry?

B. Write a sentence of your own using the words *two* and *too*.

_____

Now write a sentence using *too* and *to*.

_____

Now write a sentence using *to* and *two*.

_____

Writing a Paragraph That Explains

When you write a paragraph that explains how to do something, be sure the main idea in your topic sentence is clear. The detail sentences that follow must be in **chronological,** or **time,** order.

> EXAMPLE: *To prepare soup, open the can and pour the soup into a pot. Put the pot on the stove and turn on the heat. Stir the soup while it heats.*

It would not work to tell the reader to stir the soup before opening the can.

Suppose you wanted to plant a vegetable garden. Why would the directions in this paragraph not be too helpful?

(1) The first step in planning a vegetable garden is to look for a level spot that gets at least six hours of sun each day. (2) Just before planting the seeds, be sure to rake the ground smooth. (3) Once the garden is dug, add fertilizer to improve the soil. (4) Use a stick to make a furrow in the ground in which to plant your seeds. (5) Dig the ground to a depth of about twenty centimetres. (6) After you plant the seeds, keep the soil damp until the seeds sprout. (7) As you dig, get rid of weeds, roots, and rocks. (8) After choosing a place for your garden, decide which vegetables you would like to grow. (9) Drop the seeds into the furrow and cover them with soil. (10) The best time to water your garden is in the morning.

The writer of this paragraph has the steps for planting a garden all mixed up. Read the paragraph again carefully. The first sentence tells what the first step would be. What do you think you should do next after finding a good spot? Write the numbers of the sentences in the correct order on these lines.

_____ _____ _____ _____ _____ _____ _____ _____ _____ _____

Writing a Paragraph That Explains (continued)

Now you are ready to rewrite the paragraph. Start by writing a clear topic sentence. Then write your detail sentences in the right order. When you write the paragraph, try to use words such as *before, first, second, after, next,* and *then* to help your reader follow your directions. Edit your work to make sure you have included all the steps.

_____

_____

_____

_____

_____

_____

_____

_____

_____

_____

_____

_____

_____

EXERCISE 44 (Study Skills)
Following Directions

To follow directions you need to pay close attention to each step and you must know which way is left and which way is right.

A. Marenka works in the Valley Pet Shop in the Thornhill Shopping Centre. One day a man phoned and asked her how to get to the pet shop. Marenka gave him these directions.

> Enter from Parking Area 1.
> Go past Peter's Pizza and Lady Bug Books.
> Turn left at Goldcrest Jewellers.
> At the information booth, turn right.
> The Valley Pet Shop is straight ahead.

Follow Marenka's directions on the shopping centre map. Are they correct? Cross out the sentence that is incorrect.

B. Imagine you are waiting for your mother in Eddie's Shoe Repair. A woman asks you the way to Andy's Music. Write a paragraph in your notebook explaining clearly how to get there.

EXERCISE 45 (Word Skills)
Homonyms

Homonyms are words that sound the same but are spelled differently.

EXAMPLE: *sail – sale*   *way – weigh*   *bye – buy*

The word *homonym* comes from two Greek words, *homos* (same) and *onyma* (name).

Circle the correct homonyms in each of the following sentences.

1. The (night, knight) (through, threw) the monster into the (sea, see).

2. Whenever the wind (blue, blew), the (whole, hole) house would (creek, creak).

3. The (for, four) boys tried to open the (steel, steal) gate.

4. My (aunt, ant) uses (flower, flour) to make pies.

5. The (bare, bear) ran down the (road, rode) and into the (fir, fur) trees.

6. Megan's team (won, one) (two, too) games this (weak, week).

7. The (plain, plane) landed on the golf (course, coarse).

8. Let's leave (hour, our) (clothes, close) (hear, here).

9. Don't (break, brake) that (pain, pane) of glass.

10. Did you (by, buy) that (pale, pail) on (sale, sail)?

11. Did you see the eagle (soar, sore) before it (ate, eight) the fish.

12. Mrs. Tanaka's (son, sun) was sick with the (flu, flew) and lost (wait, weight).

13. (Where, Wear) did your mother put the (mail, male)?

EXERCISE 46 (Paragraph Construction)
Explaining with Examples

Before you start writing a paragraph, you must choose the main idea. Then you must plan the rest of the paragraph. Often the easiest way to explain a main idea is by giving **examples**.

A. Read the following paragraph carefully. The topic sentence is printed in italics. Notice how the rest of the sentences give examples to show how animals escape from trouble.

Most animals try to get away from danger as fast as possible. Some can outrun most of their attackers. The antelope, deer, horse, kangaroo, and ostrich have long legs and can cover great distances at high speeds. The rabbit bounds along at a fast speed and also makes long, zigzag jumps. Many other short-legged animals, such as the prairie dog, cannot run far at high speed. These animals rush into holes in the ground where their enemies cannot follow. Some small birds, such as sparrows, fly into thick bushes where large birds or other animals cannot go. Most birds, however, take to the air when they are frightened.

(Excerpted from *The World Book Encyclopedia* © 1990 World Book Inc. by permission.)

In the chart below, list four of the ways that animals get away from danger. Then name the animals that use this method.

Ways to Escape	Which Animals Use This Method?
1. outrun attackers	antelope, deer, horse, kangaroo, ostrich
2.	
3.	
4.	

Explaining with Examples (continued)

B. Sue enjoys writing scary stories. One day she decided to write a story about Gaplak, a very ugly monster. Before Sue started to write, she tried to imagine what Gaplak would look like. She jotted down her ideas on a piece of paper. Here is the beginning of Sue's list. Add three more ideas of your own.

1. _a huge, hairy purple wart on the end of its nose_

2. _teeth like yellow axe blades_

3. _____

4. _____

5. _____

C. Now use these ideas to write the first paragraph of Sue's story. When you have finished, check your paragraph for unity. Each sentence should give an example to prove that Gaplak really is ugly. Use the following sentence as your topic sentence.

Out of the bubbling mud came the ugliest creature I have ever seen.

_____

_____

_____

_____

_____

_____

_____

Irregular Verbs: Part 2

Remember that **irregular verbs** change their form when they are used in the past tense.

Present Tense	Past Tense	Past Participle
(Today I)	(Yesterday I)	(During the past week I)
break	broke	(have) broken
choose	chose	(have) chosen
freeze	froze	(have) frozen
speak	spoke	(have) spoken
steal	stole	(have) stolen
write	wrote	(have) written

Complete each sentence with the correct form of the verb in parentheses. Remember to use the past participle after all helping verbs.

1. The Pelly River has been _____ (freeze) since November.

2. Chessa _____ (write) to her parents last Monday.

3. Our teacher slipped on some stairs and _____ (break) his leg.

4. Did Pam know that Karl had _____ (steal) the money?

5. Yesterday Dr. Johnston _____ (speak) to us about China.

6. Have the judges _____ (choose) the winner?

7. The thieves _____ (steal) the gold bracelet.

8. Mr. Yamada has _____ (write) a book about skunks.

9. Has Ms. Shasko _____ (speak) to your parents?

10. The cucumber plants _____ (freeze) last night.

11. Antonio's hockey stick was _____ (break) during the game.

12. Molly _____ (choose) the purple backpack.

A. Add commas where they are needed in these sentences.

1. Mandy Pat and Tamara saw the huge totem pole.

2. My sister was born in Melville Saskatchewan on March 29 1977.

3. Cindy's address is 127 Belmont Avenue Pembroke Ontario K8A 2C4.

4. On May 15 1989 the bridge suddenly collapsed.

5. Are you sure Nicole that the gate is closed?

6. Chipmunks are hunted by owls hawks coyotes and bobcats.

7. Don't forget Craig that school starts on Tuesday September 2.

B. In each of the following sentences underline the noun that is the subject. Above the noun write **S** if the subject is singular, or **P** if it is plural. Circle the form of the verb that agrees with the subject.

1. Usually Mrs. Singh (leaves, leave) the keys here.

2. (Here's, Here are) your father's boots.

3. The river (has, have) risen two metres.

4. Your brothers (is, are) always late.

5. (There's, There are) two cars in the ditch.

6. The wolves (crawls, crawl) under the fence.

7. Greg and Julien (plans, plan) to play baseball.

Review (continued)

C. Complete each sentence with the correct form of the verb in parentheses. Remember to use the past participle after helping verbs. Do not use the present tense.

1. Tom _____ (take) his gym shorts home to wash.

2. The girls must have _____ (run) all the way home.

3. Has your father _____ (see) your report card?

4. By seven-thirty snow had _____ (begin) to fall.

5. Tom _____ (do) his homework on Saturday.

6. The water in the puddle was _____ (freeze).

7. The chain on my mountain bike is _____ (break).

8. Have you _____ (take) the dog for a walk today?

9. Mr. Scardillo _____ (break) his leg while skiing.

10. My mother _____ (speak) to me about getting home late.

D. Write a descriptive sentence using each of these verbs correctly.

1. froze _____

2. stolen _____

3. taken _____

4. seen _____

5. done _____

6. spoke _____

7. written _____

8. eaten _____

9. begun _____

Antonyms Are Opposites

Antonyms are words that are opposite in meaning.

EXAMPLE: old – new   right – wrong   up – down   push – pull

A. Write the antonym of each of these words.

1. shallow _____

2. happy _____

3. dirty _____

4. wet _____

5. front _____

6. strong _____

7. empty _____

8. start _____

B. Hidden in this word search are three antonyms for *dull*, five antonyms for *noisy*, and five antonyms for *slow*. Find them and write them in the proper columns.

Q	U	I	E	T	B	S	O	K
U	F	A	S	T	P	T	S	S
I	C	A	L	M	E	I	H	H
C	F	W	R	G	A	L	I	A
K	S	T	A	J	C	L	N	R
K	W	S	P	E	E	D	Y	P
E	I	L	I	H	F	C	M	U
E	F	I	D	K	U	P	G	P
N	T	M	S	I	L	E	N	T

noisy

1._____

2._____

3._____

4._____

5._____

slow

1._____

2._____

3._____

4._____

5._____

dull

1._____

2._____

3._____

EXERCISE 49 (Sentence Construction)
Choosing Verbs Carefully

The verbs in your sentences are very important. Always use verbs that help the reader to clearly *see* or *hear* what is happening.

> *EXAMPLE:* **gobble, crunch, gnaw, munch, nibble**, and **gulp** show what is happening more clearly than **eat** does.

The verbs in boldface type in the following sentences are not very interesting. In the blank at the end of each sentence, write a more descriptive verb. Make sure the verbs you choose help the reader to *see* or *hear* the action. You will find some of these verbs in the mini-thesaurus at the back of this book, which lists synonyms.

EXAMPLE: The huge snake **came** through a hole in the roof. _slithered_

1. The baseball **hit** the stone wall. _____

2. My younger brother **walked** proudly in the band. _____

3. "Don't open that window!" **said** the officer. _____

4. The huge jet **went** right over the crowd. _____

5. The large dinosaur **ran** into the swamp. _____

6. Terry **made** a model of the planets. _____

7. "Let's go to the mall!" **said** Angela. _____

8. "Alex, come inside," **called** Mother. _____

9. My uncle **took** the last cookie. _____

10. Jeremy **ate** the apple slowly. _____

EXERCISE 50 (Grammar and Usage)
Irregular Verbs: Part 3

Here are more irregular verbs to learn.

Present Tense	Past Tense	Past Participle
(Today I)	(Yesterday I)	(During the past week, I)
draw	drew	(have) drawn
tear	tore	(have) torn
wear	wore	(have) worn
fly	flew	(have) flown
blow	blew	(have) blown
grow	grew	(have) grown
know	knew	(have) known
throw	threw	(have) thrown

Complete each sentence with the correct form of the verb in parentheses(). Remember to use the past participle after all helping verbs.

1. The cat _____ (tear) the curtains.

2. The captain _____ (blow) the whistle at five o'clock.

3. Our dog has _____ (know) these tricks since she was a pup.

4. Brett has _____ (fly) that plane before.

5. Has Erin _____ (blow) up the balloons?

6. Several flocks of geese _____ (fly) over the barn.

7. Some of the football players _____ (wear) gloves.

8. Ms. Yoshida _____ (tear) the paper into strips.

9. Have you _____ (wear) your new sweater yet?

10. During the past year, Jolene has _____ (grow) ten centimetres.

11. Before he died, the old pirate had _____ (draw) a map.

12. The quarterback _____ (throw) the ball into the end zone.

Explaining with Reasons

When you write a paragraph that explains something, it is important to give reasons to help the reader understand your main idea better.

Did you know that deserts cover nearly a fifth of the Earth's land surface? Many people think that these dry lands are worthless. Actually, the deserts are very useful.

Suppose you were asked to write a paragraph about why deserts are valuable. What reasons would you use to prove that the world's deserts are really very rich lands?

Listed below are some facts about deserts. Check the six details that you could use in your paragraph.

1. One day the temperature in the Sahara Desert reached 58°C in the shade.

2. Under the deserts in Algeria, Libya, Saudi Arabia, and Kuwait are large amounts of oil.

3. My Uncle Fred once got lost in the desert.

4. Many deserts contain valuable minerals such as gold, silver, copper, nickel, and lead.

5. Date palms grow in deserts in northern Africa and southwestern Asia.

6. In the deserts of western Australia large amounts of iron ore are mined.

7. In some deserts it hasn't rained for more than ten years.

8. The Atacama Desert in South America produces nitrate, which is used to make fertilizer.

9. Diamonds are found in the deserts of southwestern Africa.

Now use the details you have checked to write your paragraph in your notebook. Start with an interesting topic sentence.

EXERCISE 52 (Word Skills)
Making New Words with Prefixes

A **prefix** is a word part. It is added to the beginning of a word to make a new word. The word that the prefix is added to is called the **base word**.

EXAMPLE:

Base Word	Prefix	New Word	New Meaning
write	re-	rewrite	to write again
kind	un-	unkind	cruel, not kind

Often you can use prefixes to figure out the meaning of new words. For example, the prefix *re-* means "again" or "once more." This information would help you to understand *rebuild* (to build again) or *repaint* (to paint again).

Here are some important prefixes for you to learn.

Prefix	Meaning	Examples
anti-	against	antifreeze, antiseptic
mis-	badly, wrongly	misspell, misunderstand
pre-	before	precook, pretest, prefabricate
re-	again, once more	recheck, reheat, relock
un-	not	unfair, unbroken, unhurt

Add one of the prefixes you have learned to each word in italics. Write the new word on the blank line. Check your answers in your dictionary to make sure they are real words.

EXAMPLE: not *locked*   __unlocked__

1. to *heat* before _____

2. to *treat* badly _____

3. not *safe* _____

4. against *slavery* _____

5. to *fill* again _____

6. to *pay* before _____

7. not *like* _____

8. to *weigh* again _____

9. to *test* before _____

10. to *behave* wrongly _____

11. not *true* _____

12. to *count* wrongly _____

13. to *open* again _____

14. not *born* _____

EXERCISE 53 (Punctuation and Capitalization)
Quotation Marks Around Exact Words

The words that tell exactly what someone says or said are called **quotations**.

> EXAMPLE: *"Come over and play," shouted Jessica.*

Quotation marks (" ") are used at the beginning and end of a quotation. Remember that quotation marks always come in pairs.

Use a comma to separate a quotation from the rest of the sentence. When the quotation is at the beginning of the sentence, put the comma inside the second set of quotation marks.

> EXAMPLE: *"I wish I'd never come," replied Ryan nervously.*

In the following sentences underline the exact words of the speaker. Then punctuate the sentences correctly.

1. Give him something to play with suggested Uncle Will.

2. I'm cold said Debra as she reached for the blanket.

3. Perhaps I'd better go with you answered Mr. Hillman.

4. Open your mouth wide ordered the dentist.

5. I hope you know what you're doing grumbled the old man.

6. Now we're getting somewhere said the detective.

7. I was just thinking the same thing remarked Ms. Keenan.

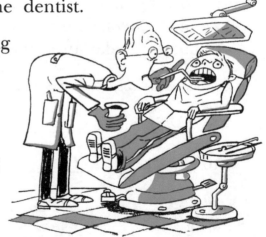

8. Of course not replied Josie angrily.

9. I think the whole idea is silly muttered Wally.

10. We've got to do something insisted Martika.

11. I wish the dog next door would stop barking complained Father.

EXERCISE 54 (Sentence Construction)
Combining Simple Sentences

You can make a **compound sentence** by joining pairs of simple sentences with the words *and*, *or*, and *but* using these rules.

1. Use **and** when the second sentence gives added information.

*EXAMPLE: Bob walked quickly up the street, **and** Shawn hurried after him.*

2. Use **or** when the second sentence gives a choice.

*EXAMPLE: Turn the heat down, **or** the fudge will burn.*

3. Use **but** when the second sentence has an opposite or different idea.

*EXAMPLE: Becky was here before nine o'clock, **but** Ingrid did not arrive until noon.*

Make your own compound sentences by joining each pair of simple sentences.

1. Suddenly there was a loud bang. All the chickens raced for the shed.

_____

_____

2. Derek waited for thirty minutes. The bus for Dawson Creek did not arrive.

_____

_____

3. The rain must stop before noon. The game will be cancelled.

_____

_____

4. The message was written in a secret code. Denise soon figured it out.

_____

_____

Antonym Puzzles

Remember that an antonym is a word that means the opposite of another word.

A. In each sentence, fill in the blank with an antonym that rhymes with the word in italics.

EXAMPLE: Young is to *old* as hot is to <u>cold</u>

1. Wrong is to *right* as heavy is to _____.

2. Wild is to *tame* as different is to _____.

3. Weak is to *strong* as right is to _____.

4. Large is to *tiny* as dull is to _____.

5. Early is to *late* as love is to _____.

6. High is to *low* as fast is to _____.

7. Dead is to *alive* as leave is to _____.

8. Dirty is to *clean* as king is to _____.

9. Lose is to *find* as cruel is to _____.

10. Far is to *near* as there is to _____.

11. Short is to *tall* as spring is to _____.

12. Sell is to *buy* as wet is to _____.

B. Using the same pattern, try writing two sentences of your own.

1. _____ is to _____

as _____ is to _____.

2. _____ is to _____

as _____ is to _____.

Quotations at the End of the Sentence

In Exercise 53 you learned how to punctuate sentences that begin with quotations. Sometimes quotations come at the end of the sentence. When this happens, put the comma *just before* the first set of quotation marks. Remember to always begin the quotation with an upper-case letter.

EXAMPLE: *Kim replied, "Don't worry about me."*

A. In each of these sentences underline the exact words of the speaker. Then punctuate the sentences correctly. Circle any letters that should be capitalized.

EXAMPLE: Ms. Ishimoto laughed and said, "he didn't give it to me."

1. The old man replied perhaps I should leave now.

2. Vicki thought for a minute and then said let's go.

3. Mrs. O'Haloran said that's just what I've been thinking.

4. Robina whispered close the door.

5. Suddenly the stranger jumped up and said I must leave.

B. Some of the quotations in these sentences are at the end. Others are at the beginning. Underline the exact words of the speaker. Then punctuate the sentences correctly.

1. I can't remember what happened mumbled Josh.

2. On Thursday we will be in Whitehorse answered Jessica.

3. After looking at the menu Matt said I think I will have fish and chips.

4. Perhaps you left your backpack on the bus said Jenny.

5. We never thought of that mumbled Inga.

6. Ashley said please pass me the pepper.

UNIT
15

Pronouns Replace Nouns

Nouns are words that name people, animals, places, and things. Sometimes we use words to take the place of nouns. Read these sentences. Which nouns do each of the words in boldface type replace?

Mario Lemieux scored the goal.	**He** scored the goal.
Give Haley the money.	Give **her** the money.
The pie was delicious.	**It** was delicious.
The girls ate the whole watermelon.	**They** ate the whole watermelon.

Words such as *he*, *she*, *her*, *him*, *it*, *them*, and *they* are called pronouns.
A **pronoun** is a word that takes place of a noun.

Rewrite these sentences. Replace the words in boldface type with pronouns.

EXAMPLE: **Judy** left suddenly.   She left suddenly.

1. **Andy** is always giggling.

   _____

2. Give **Olivia and Jasmine** the message.

   _____

3. **Maria** broke her arm playing hockey.

   _____

4. Put **the shovels** in the garage.

   _____

5. Let **Ethan** open the door.

   _____

6. **Jessica and Lauren** are on the swim team.

   _____

7. Hang **your jacket** in the closet.

   _____

EXERCISE 58 (Sentence Construction)
Pronouns Make Your Writing Smoother

Pronouns let us talk about someone or something without repeating the same noun.

> *EXAMPLE: Cathy asked **Cathy's** uncle whether **Cathy's uncle** had seen
> **Cathy's** jacket.*
>
> *Cathy asked **her** uncle whether **he** had seen **her** jacket.*

When you replace the nouns in boldface type with pronouns the sentence is shorter and smoother.

Rewrite the following paragraph. Improve it by replacing the nouns in boldface type with pronouns that fit.

Last summer Amy and Eric visited **Amy and Eric's** Aunt Julia in Queensland, Australia. **Aunt Julia** took **Amy and Eric** to the Currumbin Bird Sanctuary. **Amy and Eric** saw thousands of brightly coloured parrots. **The parrots** were used to visitors and ate from Amy and Eric's hands. In the afternoon **Amy and Eric** went swimming in the ocean. **The ocean** was warm and clear. Then Aunt Julia took **Amy and Eric** to **Aunt Julia's** favourite restaurant for supper.

_____

_____

_____

_____

_____

_____

_____

_____

Using Prefixes to Make Antonyms

Often you can make the antonym, or opposite of a word, by adding a prefix. Three common prefixes that work this way are *un-*, *in-*, and *dis-*.

EXAMPLE: true – **un**true   visible – **in**visible   like – **dis**like

Before words that begin with the letter *p*, change the spelling of *in-* to *im-*.

EXAMPLE: possible – **im**possible

The prefix *non-* means "not" or "the opposite of."

EXAMPLE: We took a **nonstop** flight from Calgary to London, England.

A. Make the antonym of each of these words by adding the prefix *un-*, *in-* (*im-*), or *dis-*. Use your dictionary if you are not sure which prefix is correct.

EXAMPLE: fair _unfair_

1. honest _____
2. able _____
3. patient _____
4. happy _____
5. complete _____
6. lock _____

7. obey _____
8. roll _____
9. polite _____
10. necessary _____
11. sane _____
12. load _____

B. Use each of the following words in an interesting sentence. Use your dictionary if you are not sure of the meaning of a word.

1. nonsense _____
2. non-fiction _____
3. non-poisonous _____
4. non-swimmer _____

Making Pronouns Agree

Like nouns, pronouns may be either singular or plural. Here is a list of common pronouns. Notice that *you* and *your* may be either singular or plural.

Singular Pronouns	Plural Pronouns
I, me, my	we, us, our
you, your	you, your
he, him, his,	they, them, their
she, her, hers	they, them, their
it, its	they, them, their

Always make sure your pronouns match, or **agree** with, the noun they replace.

1. If the pronoun takes the place of a singular noun, use a singular pronoun.

*EXAMPLE: When my **brother** heard the ghost open the door, **he** hid under the bed.*

2. If the pronoun takes the place of a plural noun, use a plural pronoun.

*EXAMPLE: When my **brothers** heard the ghost open the door, **they** hid under the bed.*

UNIT 16

Fill in the blanks in these sentences with **he**, **she**, **his**, **her**, **it**, **they**, **their**, or **them**. Draw an arrow from the pronoun to the noun it replaces.

EXAMPLE: When my parents visited Nunavut, _____they_____ saw some Inuit art.

1. Our cat scratches on the window when _____ wants to come in.

2. Please tell the girls that _____ must leave now.

3. Because Pierre slept in, _____ missed the bus.

4. My aunt left _____ umbrella at the mall.

5. Do the boys have _____ uniforms?

6. Pick up the books and put _____ on the shelf.

EXERCISE 61 (Composition Construction)

Writing a Friendly Letter

Letters that are written to good friends and relatives are called **friendly letters**. A friendly letter has five parts. Here is how a friendly letter should be organized.

1. **Heading**
   (your address and the date)

2. **Salutation**
   (followed by a comma)

3. **Body**
   (tell your friend what you would say if you were with her or him)

4. **Closing**
   (use a comma and capitalize the first word only)

5. **Signature**
   (sign your name clearly)

> 1824 Chestnut Street
> Victoria, BC V8R 4N5
> April 29, 2003
>
> Dear Olga,
>   Our family will be going camping in Manning Park during the first two weeks of July. Manning Park is in the mountains about two hundred kilometres east of Vancouver. Dad said I could bring one of my friends. Would you like to come?
>   We had a fantastic time in Manning Park last year. Every morning my brother and I got up early to fish in Lightning Lake. After breakfast we went swimming or canoeing. There are many interesting trails to explore near the campground.
>   I know you would really enjoy Manning Park. There are so many interesting things to do. Be sure to bring your fishing rod and camera.
>
>   Your friend,
>   Kim-Lan Chan

When you write a friendly letter, keep these points in mind.
1. Start the heading a little to the right of the middle of the page.
2. Skip a space between the heading and the salutation.
3. Skip a space between the last line of the body and the closing.
4. Start the closing directly under the first letter or number in the heading.

Writing a Friendly Letter (continued)

Imagine that your family is going on vacation. Write an interesting letter to a friend asking whether he or she would like to come with you. Use Kim-Lan's letter as a model. In the first paragraph, tell your friend where you are going. In the second paragraph, talk about what you will be doing. In the third paragraph, explain why you would like your friend to come.

_____

_____

_____

_____

_____

_____

_____

_____

_____

_____

_____

_____

_____

_____

EXERCISE 62 (Punctuation and Capitalization)
Quotation Marks with Questions and Exclamations

When a quotation is a question or an exclamation, remember to use a question mark or an exclamation mark.

> EXAMPLE: *"What are we going to do?" asked Denise.*
> *Denise asked, "What are we going to do?"*
>
> *"I've caught a huge fish!" shouted Jason excitedly.*
> *Jason shouted excitedly, "I've caught a huge fish!"*

Notice that the question mark or exclamation mark is always placed *inside* the final pair of quotation marks. If the quotation begins the sentence, the question mark or exclamation mark takes the place of the comma.

Punctuate these sentences correctly.

1. Whom are you waiting for asked Ms. Petrovich

2. Throw the ball screamed Britta

3. Now what are we going to do cried Carlos

4. Dana asked are you walking home today

5. I hate that medicine grumbled Jeremy

6. Quit teasing me shrieked Beth

7. Have you seen this book before asked Miss Melcher

8. Just wait till I catch you thundered the giant

9. Would you like some chocolate ice cream said Hiroko

10. Let's stop for a rest gasped Mario

11. Did you see someone run down the lane asked the fire chief

12. Where were you this afternoon asked Mr. Murakami

EXERCISE 63 (Punctuation and Capitalization)

Divided Quotations

Quotations that are split into two parts are called **divided quotations**.

EXAMPLE: *"I've decided," said Jackie, "to do my homework."*
"Don't talk too loudly," whispered Simon, "or you'll wake Jodi."

Notice that quotation marks are used before and after each part of a divided quotation. An upper-case letter is used only at the beginning of the quotation. The first word in the second part of a divided quotation starts with a lower-case letter. Pay close attention to where the commas are placed.

Circle the name of the person who is speaking in each sentence. Underline the exact words the speaker says. Then punctuate the sentences correctly. Circle any letters that should be capitalized.

1. the storm last night said andrea frightened everyone

2. well said dan i guess that ends the game

3. unless the rain stops soon explained the umpire the game will be cancelled

4. be quiet tyler snapped mr neilson you're disturbing everyone

5. this crossword puzzle grumbled patsy is very difficult

6. if we leave now suggested sakina we can catch the boat for charlottetown

7. because the dog barked all night complained wally i couldn't sleep

8. i am sure replied the doctor that it's not serious

9. you can be sure promised brandon that we'll be there

10. when the bell rings explained mrs murphy you may put your books away

11. i believe you replied erica but do you think mr goldberg will

12. if i were you said shannon i'd go anyway

UNIT
17

EXERCISE 64 (Sentence Construction)
Changing Sentence Patterns

The usual place for the subject is at the beginning of the sentence.

EXAMPLE: **A strange creature** *suddenly appeared from inside the spacecraft.*

To make your writing more interesting, try putting the subject in a different place sometimes. Often you can put the subject inside the predicate.

EXAMPLE: *Suddenly* **a strange creature** *appeared from inside the spacecraft.*

Sometimes the subject can be moved to the end of the sentence.

EXAMPLE: *Suddenly from inside the spacecraft appeared* **a strange creature.**

In each sentence the subject is at the beginning. Rewrite each sentence, moving the subject to a different place.

1. The black colt raced into the barn.

   _____

2. Ramaz played the trumpet in the band on Saturday.

   _____

3. Nadia scored two goals in the final twenty seconds.

   _____

4. The frightened mouse darted into its hole.

   _____

5. A huge spider crawled out from under the suitcase.

   _____

6. The girls woke up at about six o'clock.

   _____

7. The herd of wild horses raced across the prairie.

   _____

EXERCISE 65 (Grammar and Usage)
Using Pronouns Correctly: Part 1

Read these sentences. Which noun does each pronoun in boldface type replace?

Harry is the captain of the team. **He** is the captain of the team.

The dogs chased the cat up the tree. **They** chased the cat up the tree.

Words such as *he* and *they* are called **subject pronouns**. They take the place of the noun that is the subject. Five other pronouns that can be used as subjects are *I, she, you, it,* and *we*.

Be very careful when the subject is a noun and a pronoun. Which of these sentences sounds correct to you?

Mom and I visited Nova Scotia. **Mom and me** visited Nova Scotia.

If you are not sure, read the sentences without the words *Mom and*. You will quickly see that *I*, not *me*, is the correct pronoun to use.

Write the correct pronoun in the blank at the right. Test each sentence by reading it without the noun and the word *and*.

1. Debbie and (they, them) painted the fence. _____

2. My grandfather and (she, her) washed the dishes. _____

3. Marcus and (him, he) chopped the wood. _____

4. Lee-Ming and (she, her) won a trip to the Yukon. _____

5. Tyrone and (them, they) went to the hockey game. _____

6. Jenna and (I, me) must leave before eight o'clock. _____

7. Last week Danielle and (her, she) walked to school. _____

8. Jake and (him, he) played softball on Saturday. _____

9. My aunt and (I, me) won the three-legged race. _____

10. Our cousins from India and (us, we) went to the museum. _____

11. Ms. Lopez and (they, them) put away the books. _____

12. After school Zinta and (he, him) chased the cat. _____

Writing Postcards

When we are on vacation, we often write postcards instead of letters. A postcard usually has a picture on one side. The other side is divided into two parts. The left side is for your message. The right side is for the address.

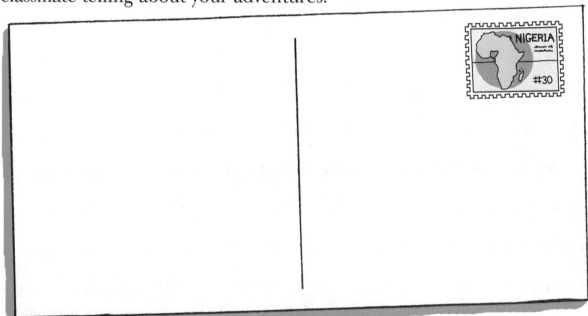

July 10, 2002

Dear Jeremy,
    Today we visited Niagara Falls. The water really thunders over the edge. In the afternoon my sister and I took a ride on the *Maid of the Mist*. This boat takes you right up to the main falls. Tomorrow we're driving to Toronto to see Ontario Place and the CN Tower.

                    Cory

Jeremy Gellner
267 Brock Road
Yellowknife, NT X1A 1Z5

Imagine that you are on a journey across Africa. Write a postcard to a classmate telling about your adventures.

NIGERIA #30

EXERCISE 67 (Sentence Construction)

New Ways to Begin

In Lesson 64 you learned that sentences do not always need to begin with the subject. Another way to make your sentences more interesting is to start with a group of words that tells where something happened.

> EXAMPLE: **At the edge of the pool** sat a large penguin.

You can also start sentences with a word that tells *how* something happened. These words often end in *-ly*.

> EXAMPLE: **Angrily** Janice marched out of the room.

A. Write four sentences that begin by telling *where*. Some good words to start with are *behind, above, below, over, between, under,* and *near*.

1. _____

_____

2. _____

_____

3. _____

_____

B. Now write four sentences that begin by telling how. Try starting with some of these words: *carefully, slowly, quickly, quietly, bravely, nervously, cautiously, patiently, gently, hungrily.*

1. _____

_____

2. _____

_____

3. _____

_____

UNIT
18

EXERCISE 68 (Grammar and Usage)
Using Pronouns Correctly: Part 2

The pronouns *I, he, she, it, we, you,* and *they* are called **subject pronouns**. They are used in the subject part of the sentence.

The pronouns *me, him, her, us,* and *them* are usually found in the predicate. Often they come after an action verb. These pronouns are called **object pronouns**.

Subject Pronouns	Object Pronouns
I helped Kurt.	Kurt helped **me**.
He invited Aunt Sylvia.	Aunt Sylvia invited **him**.
She tagged Amber.	Amber tagged **her**.
They told Nathan.	Nathan told **them**.
We asked the girls.	The girls asked **us**.
You lent Rachel five dollars.	Rachel lent **you** five dollars.
It scared Devin.	Devin scared **it**.

Notice that two of the pronouns *you* and *it* do not change form.

Decide whether the blanks in these sentences should have a subject pronoun or an object pronoun. Write **S** in front of the sentence if it needs a subject pronoun. Write **O** if it needs an object pronoun. Then choose the correct pronoun from the parentheses that follow each blank.

EXAMPLE: <u>S</u> <u>He</u> (He, Him) collects hockey cards.

_____ 1. The coach gave _____ (she, her) a new uniform.

_____ 2. The dog followed _____ (I, me) to school.

_____ 3. Justin invited _____ (they, them) to his birthday party.

_____ 4. Ms. Chung and _____ (we, us) went ice skating.

_____ 5. My brother found _____ (they, them) under his bed.

_____ 6. My father and _____ (he, him) shovelled the snow off the driveway.

_____ 7. The police officer asked _____ (she, her) some questions.

EXERCISE 69 (Grammar and Usage)
Using Pronouns Correctly: Part 3

Sometimes a noun and a pronoun follow an action verb.

EXAMPLE: The dog followed **Neil and him** to school.

If you are not sure which pronoun to use, always read the sentence without the noun and the word "*and.*"

EXAMPLE: My cousin pushed Cara and (I, me) into the pool.
My cousin pushed (I, me) into the pool.
My cousin pushed **Cara and me** into the pool.

A. In each of the following sentences choose the correct pronoun and write it in the blank. Check each sentence by reading it without the noun and the word *and.*

EXAMPLE: Aunt Celia took Inga and (we, us) to the circus. _____us_____

1. Mrs. Schmidt asked Laura and (she, her) to sing. _____

2. Uncle Norman taught Trevor and (I, me) to swim. _____

3. The principal called Gavin and (him, he) into her office. _____

4. Mr. Imada loaned Ben and (they, them) his boat. _____

5. The bright light blinded Henry and (him, he). _____

6. Mr. Lee gave Joe and (we, us) the keys. _____

B. Write sentences of your own using each group of words after an action verb.

1. Jill and me _____

2. Mr. Wong and them _____

3. the cat and her _____

4. my aunt and us _____

Working with Suffixes

A **suffix** is a word part that is added to the end of a word to change its meaning or to make a new word.

> *EXAMPLE:* use + less = useless   mouth + ful = mouthful   farm + er = farmer
>
> The suffix *-less* means "without."
>
> *EXAMPLE:* If a liquid is **colourless**, it is without colour. A **homeless** person is a person without a home.

A. Each of the following groups has a base, a prefix, and a suffix. Decide which is the prefix, which is the base, and which is the suffix. Use the three parts to form a word. Be sure to spell each word correctly. Sometimes you may have to add or delete a letter.

EXAMPLE: ed lock un <u>unlocked</u>

1. obey dis ed _____

2. ing wrap un _____

3. ly un friend _____

4. ed re place _____

B. Decide what each word in the box below means. Then write interesting sentences using three of them correctly.

hairless	spotless
fearless	endless
penniless	harmless
hopeless	worthless
cloudless	careless

_____

_____

_____

A. Punctuate these sentences correctly. Circle any letters that should be capitalized.

1. stop that man shouted the guards

2. when you leave said ms. oliver be sure to lock the door

3. where did you put the football asked amy

4. someone is coming whispered steven nervously

5. who broke the mirror asked tyler

6. detective balaski thought for a minute and then said did you hear a noise about six o'clock

7. are you sure asked hannah that you know how to use that camera

8. i hope replied marty that christopher gets here on time

B. In each of the following sentences choose the correct pronoun and write it in the blank. Check each sentence by reading it without the noun and the word *and.*

1. We told Julia and (she, her) our story. _____

2. Uncle Eric drove June and (they, them) to the arena. _____

3. (He, Him) and Dylan won the three-legged race. _____

4. On Thursday, we saw Dennis and (he, him) at the park. _____

5. Mrs. Quan gave Emily and (I, me) a ride to school. _____

6. Austin and (I, me) are ready to go. _____

7. Amber showed Jill and (they, them) the way to the beach. _____

8. Ms. Mills helped Gurdeep and (her, she) to fix the bicycle. _____

Review (continued)

C. Join each of the following pairs of simple sentences with the words **or**, **but**, or **and**.

1. Brittany plays the guitar. Her brother Adam plays the banjo.

   _____

2. I like the red jacket. Julia prefers the blue one.

   _____

3. The rain must stop in fifteen minutes. The game will be cancelled.

   _____

4. My room is tidy. My brother's room is a mess.

   _____

D. Some of the following word pairs are synonyms. Others are antonyms. Write **S** in the blanks following the pairs that are synonyms. Write **A** in the blanks following the pairs that are antonyms.

1. slow – fast   _____   4. difficult – easy   _____

2. glad – pleased   _____   5. prison – jail   _____

3. end – finish   _____   6. moving – still   _____

E. Fill in the blanks in these sentences with **he**, **she**, **his**, **her**, **it**, **they**, **their**, or **them**. Draw an arrow from the pronoun to the noun it replaces.

1. My brother forgot _____ jacket at school yesterday.

2. Pick the apples and put _____ in the box.

3. Please tell Ian and Luis that _____ should come for lunch.

4. Have the girls made _____ beds?

5. Emma told _____ brother the good news.

EXERCISE 71 (Sentence Construction)
More Practice with Combining Sentences

One way you can improve your work so that a paragraph reads more smoothly is by combining short sentences.

Join each of the following pairs of sentences to make one stronger sentence.

1. I left my backpack at the park. I left my jacket there too.

   _____

2. Elsa went skiing yesterday. Tinisha went with her.

   _____

3. Amrit and I bought a model of the space station. We put it together.

   _____

   _____

4. The ambulance raced down the street. The ambulance stopped in front of our school.

   _____

   _____

5. An elephant's skin is thick. An elephant's skin is dark grey.

   _____

6. The squirrel raced across the road. The squirrel scrambled up the maple tree.

   _____

   _____

EXERCISE 72 (Grammar and Usage)
Using Pronouns Correctly: Part 4

Words such as *under*, *behind*, *between*, and *with* are called **prepositions**. Often prepositions show direction or position.

Here is a list of words that are often used as prepositions.

about	around	between	in	out	toward
above	at	beyond	into	outside	under
across	before	by	near	over	until
after	behind	down	of	past	up
against	below	during	off	since	upon
along	beneath	for	on	through	with
among	beside	from	onto	to	without

After a preposition, always use an object pronoun: *me*, *him*, *her*, *us*, *them*, *you*, or *it*.

*EXAMPLE: The dog ran toward **Mary**.*
*The dog ran toward **her**.*

Sometimes the pronoun takes the place of more than one noun.

*EXAMPLE: The bus left without **Doug and Cliff**.*
*The bus left without **them**.*

Be careful when the preposition is followed by a noun and a pronoun. In the following sentences the pronouns are used correctly.

*EXAMPLE: Colleen usually walked to school with Ruth and **me**.*
*Will you be going with Tony and **him**?*

 in the box   *behind* the box   *under* the box

 on the box   *beside* the box   *between* the boxes

Using Pronouns Correctly: Part 4 (continued)

A. Rewrite each group of words. Replace the nouns with object pronouns.

EXAMPLE: near Maria <u>near her</u>

   1. to Mr. Williams   _____

   2. over the car   _____

   3. by Rachel and Paulo   _____

   4. with the horses   _____

B. Write the correct pronoun in the blank at the right. Test each sentence by reading it without the noun and the word *and*.

   1. The angry elephant charged toward Alanna and (I, me). _____

   2. Aunt Kathy played baseball with Travis and (we, us). _____

   3. Who's sitting between Teresa and (her, she)? _____

   4. Are you coming with Angie and (me, I)? _____

   5. They sat beside Dustin and (him, he). _____

C. Read each sentence carefully. If the sentence needs a subject pronoun, write **S** at the beginning of the sentence. If the sentence needs an object pronoun, write **O** at the beginning. Then write the correct pronoun for each sentence in the blank in the sentence. Test each sentence by reading it without the noun and the word *and*.

___ 1. (Her, She) and _____ (I, me) go home for lunch.

___ 2. Denise went to Goose Bay with Samantha and _____ (she, her).

___ 3. The team and _____ (we, us) are leaving now.

___ 4. Olivia and _____ (me, I) are on the soccer team.

___ 5. I have a surprise for you and _____ (he, him).

Punctuating Divided Questions

Sometimes divided quotations are questions.

> *EXAMPLE:* *"Are you sure," asked Deanna, "that you know the way?"*
> *"But why," replied Graham, "didn't you tell me?"*

These two sentences are punctuated correctly.

A. Circle the speaker in each of these sentences. Underline the exact words that the person says. Then punctuate the sentences correctly. Circle any letters that should be capitalized.

1. what will you do asked rebecca if the bus doesn't arrive

2. do you know said the taxi driver where mr chan lives

3. well replied kristen why don't we get started

4. if it doesn't rain suggested marlene can we go biking

5. are you sure asked mother that your room is tidy

B. Each of these sentences has a direct quotation. Rewrite each sentence using a divided quotation. Be sure to punctuate your work correctly.

1. I did not want to leave until you came back explained Dana.

_____

_____

2. Are you sure that your parents won't worry asked Brandon.

_____

_____

3. No, let's take the bus replied Marco.

_____

_____

EXERCISE 74 (Word Skills)
Homonym Crossword

Remember that **homonyms** are words that sound the same but have different meanings.

Fill in the crossword with homonyms for the clues given.

Across

1 not
4 teem
7 whole
8 wee
9 two, too
10 alter
11 hear
13 steel
14 sew, sow
16 right

18 read (past tense)
19 know
21 four
22 pair, pare
23 heal
24 see
26 owe
27 inn
29 buy
30 caught

31 loan
32 eye
33 breaks

Down

1 nose
2 knew
3 through
4 tee
5 meet
6 wood

12 ate
15 won
17 their, they're
20 or, ore
21 flower
22 pale
25 aunts
28 know
29 bee

EXERCISE 75 (Word Skills)
Confusing Pairs of Words

In English, some pairs of words are confusing because they look and sound almost the same. You may have already learned some of these problem words. Study carefully those you are not sure of.

Word Pairs	Meaning	Example
1. **desert**	a dry land where few plants grow	A *desert* is often sandy or stony.
dessert	food served at the end of a meal	Anna had raisin pie for *dessert*.
2. **loose**	not fastened or tight	Turn the horse *loose*.
lose	not to be able to find something	Did you *lose* your lunch?
	to be beaten	They might *lose* the game.
3. **quiet**	not making much sound	Be *quiet* and listen.
quite	very much or completely	Are you *quite* sure it was Julia?
4. **weather**	what it looks like outside	Today the *weather* is sunny.
whether	if	Do you know *whether* Amy came?

Six of these sentences contain an error. Cross out the incorrect word and write your correction above it. Put a check mark (✔) in front of the two correct sentences.

1. The button on my sweater is lose.

2. Ming did not know weather she could go.

3. On Sunday, we often have chocolate cake for desert.

4. The wind is quiet cold today.

5. For dessert, we had apple pie and ice cream.

6. Where did Roberto loose his wallet?

7. Last week, the whether was cloudy and wet.

8. Are you quite sure you did not leave your keys at home?

EXERCISE 76 (Composition Construction)
The Time Order of a Story

To write an interesting story, you must plan carefully. A good way to begin is by listing all the events in the story. Then arrange them in the order in which they happen. This is called **time order**.

On July 16, 1969, the *Apollo II* spaceship blasted off from Cape Kennedy. Four days later it landed on the moon. The following nine sentences tell what happened on the first day. Which event do you think happened first? What probably took place next? In your notebook rewrite the story, putting the sentences in the correct order.

1. Finally there were only a few seconds before blast-off.

2. An elevator took them quickly up to the spacecraft.

3. In two and a half minutes it was out of sight.

4. On the day of the flight the astronauts were up early for breakfast.

5. *Apollo II* was off to the moon!

6. With a tremendous roar, the huge rocket began to move slowly upward.

7. They strapped themselves into their seats.

8. Bright orange flames suddenly shot from the powerful engines.

9. After eating, they put on their spacesuits and large bubble helmets.

UNIT
20

EXERCISE 77 (Composition Construction)
Understanding Plot

The plan of a story is called a **plot**. A strong plot is usually made up of four parts.

1. **A beginning**

   The beginning must catch the reader's attention. It tells *who* the story is about. It tells *where* the story happens. It tells *when* the story takes place.

2. **A problem**

   The story tells about some problems the main character must solve. In the story *The Three Little Pigs*, for example, the pigs must outwit the wolf.

3. **A struggle or conflict**

   The struggle, or conflict, tells how the characters in the story try to solve the problem. The three little pigs tried to solve their problem by moving to stronger and stronger houses.

4. **A climax**

   The climax is the most exciting part of the story, when the problem is finally resolved. In *The Three Little Pigs*, the climax comes when the wolf falls into the boiling water.

Now read the story on the opposite page and see whether you can find the four parts of the plot in this story. Then answer the following questions.

1. Where and when does this story take place?

   _____

2. What problem must Tim solve?

   _____

3. How does he try to solve this problem?

   _____

   _____

4. What is the climax of the story?

   _____

   _____

Understanding Plot (continued)

It had been four months since the spaceship had blasted off from Earth. Tim was getting tired but still had a long trip before he reached Io, one of Jupiter's moons. Suddenly a strange object appeared on the radar screen. Tim checked his charts. Nothing should be near the ship. The blip on the screen was getting larger very quickly and was heading straight for his spacecraft.

Tim quickly gave the computer a command to send out an emergency electronic signal that would let any spacecraft in the area know he was there. But the blip on the radar screen kept right on coming toward his ship. Maybe the other craft's system couldn't receive his signal.

He watched for a few more seconds, then decided to start the port rockets. That would move the ship to the side. Tim slapped the switch and pushed the control lever forward. Nothing happened. Quickly he repeated the procedure. Again nothing happened. The object had not changed course. They would collide in about thirty seconds.

Frantically he hit the switch again. He could feel the thrust as the craft moved slowly to starboard. Tim breathed a sigh of relief. In a flash, the object streaked by. But in that brief moment, Tim saw five strange creatures in the foreign spaceship heading straight toward Earth.

EXERCISE 78 (Composition Construction)
Writing a Story

As well as using time order and plot, writing a good story involves the other techniques you have already learned, such as a good topic sentence, interesting detail sentences, and exact nouns, verbs, and adjectives.

Imagine that you are the first astronaut to land on the planet Olika. As you leave your spaceship, you can see what looks like a city in the distance.

Write a story about your adventures on Olika. Plan your story in two paragraphs. In the first paragraph tell about your trip from the spacecraft to the city. In the second paragraph explain what happens after you arrive. The climax of your story should come at the end of the second paragraph.

_____

_____

_____

_____

_____

_____

_____

_____

_____

_____

Using a Thesaurus

A **thesaurus** (thuh saw' rus) is a dictionary of synonyms and antonyms. The word *thesaurus* comes from a Greek word meaning "storehouse."

A complete thesaurus will list thousands of entries. In a thesaurus, the entry words are in boldface type and are arranged in alphabetical order.

The mini-thesaurus at the back of this book contains only the most common words. If you cannot find your word, look in a regular thesaurus.

A. Use the mini-thesaurus in the back of this book and your dictionary to help you answer these questions.

1. Find the word *cry* in the thesaurus. Which of these synonyms could you use to describe the sound a baby makes?

   _____

2. Study the list of synonyms for the word *move*. Which of these words could you use to describe the way a cheetah might move when chasing an antelope?

   _____

B. Although all the words listed after the entry word in a thesaurus are synonyms, they may not all have *exactly* the same meaning. Use your dictionary to check the exact meaning of the words.

1. The words *sob* and *bawl* are both listed as synonyms for *cry*. Write interesting sentences using *sob* and *bawl* correctly.

   _____

   _____

2. Suppose you wanted to describe someone who had walked for two hours through a heavy rainstorm without a jacket or coat. Which two of the synonyms for the entry word *wet* would be the best choice? Be ready to explain the reason for your choices.

   _____

EXERCISE 80 (Composition Construction)
Writing Conversations

When you use conversation, be sure to punctuate correctly. There are two rules to remember.

1. Start a new paragraph each time the speaker changes.
2. If a quotation is made up of several sentences, put one set of quotation marks at the beginning of the first sentence. The second set goes at the end of the last sentence.

In many parts of Canada, rivers freeze over during the winter. Often the ice is so strong that people can walk across it. Sometimes cars and even heavy trucks can be driven over the river on the ice. Before trying to cross a frozen river or lake, however, it is very important to make sure the ice is thick enough.

Betsy Byars has written many children's stories. One of her books is *Good-bye, Chicken Little*. This story begins with a conversation between Jimmie and his friend, Conrad. Jimmie is standing beside the clothes dryer, waiting for his jeans to dry. Conrad bursts in to tell him about Uncle Pete. Here is the beginning of the story.

Jimmie spun around. "Will you close that door? I am standing here in my underwear."

"Your uncle's getting ready to walk across the Monday River!" his friend Conrad shouted. He was panting for breath.

It was Conrad who brought Jimmie most of his bad news, and all of it in a loud, excited and—it seemed to Jimmie—happy voice.

"What?" Jimmie asked. He put one hand on the dryer for support. The dryer was so old that it trembled with every rotation.

"Come on! Some men in Harry's Bar and Grill bet your uncle he couldn't walk across the river and he's going to try."

"But the ice is too thin. He'll fall through."

"*You* know that. I know that. The men at *Harry's* know that. But your uncle—"

With this short conversation, Ms. Byars quickly gets our attention. We are eager to read the rest of the story. We want to know if Uncle Pete will fall through the ice.

Writing Conversations (continued)

Now write what you think
happens next in this story.
Make your story interesting by

- using conversation wherever
  possible (have each character
  speak more than once).
- using verbs such as *screamed,*
  shouted, and *bragged* to tell
  exactly how the characters
  speak.
- using words such as *slowly, carefully,* and *fearfully* to explain how the
  characters move and talk.

_____

_____

_____

_____

_____

_____

_____

_____

_____

_____

_____

_____

EXERCISE 81 (Grammar and Usage)
Using Adjectives to Describe

A word that describes a noun is called an **adjective**. Usually adjectives answer one of these questions:

1. What kind? a *noisy* seagull, a *spotted* salamander, the *sharp* scissors
2. How many? *several* guitars, a *few* monkeys, *sixteen* coconuts
   or
   How much? *some* sheep, *more* pepper, *less* sugar
3. Which one? *this* peach, *that* seaplane, *these* hammers, *those* parrots
4. Whose?   *my* saddle, *his* jacket, *our* corn, *their* bees

Circle the adjectives in these sentences. Then draw an arrow from each adjective to the noun it describes. The number in parentheses tells how many adjectives are in the sentence.

EXAMPLE: The powerful yellow bulldozer pushed the large rocks off the road. (3)

1. The huge waves crashed against the old wooden boat. (3)

2. Through the tall grass crept the hungry tiger. (2)

3. This soup needs more salt. (2)

4. The small grey mouse had large eyes and a pointed nose. (4)

5. Those boys live in that brick house. (3)

6. The enormous rhinoceros had two curved horns. (3)

7. Your brown sweater is in the top drawer. (3)

8. The large rubber raft disappeared under the muddy water. (3)

9. Aunt Laura gave Maya some long yellow socks. (3)

10. All spiders have eight legs. (2)

Building Interesting Sentences with Adjectives

Always choose your adjectives carefully to give your reader a clear idea of what you are talking about. Which sentence gives a clearer picture of what happened? Why?

The dog chased the rabbit.

The huge dog chased the terrified rabbit.

A. Write an adjective to describe each noun. Be sure the words you choose are interesting and descriptive. Use a different adjective with each noun.

1. a _____ boxcar

2. a _____ pigeon

3. a _____ snowdrift

4. a _____ fence post

5. a _____ shark

6. a _____ bubble

7. a _____ trumpet

8. a _____ spider

9. a _____ fire engine

10. a _____ bulldozer

11. a _____ pumpkin

12. a _____ ant

B. Using the nouns and adjectives in Exercise A, write four sentences of your own.

1. _____

_____

2. _____

_____

3. _____

_____

4. _____

_____

EXERCISE 83 (Composition Construction)
More Practice with Stories

Remember that to write an interesting story you need to use time order, plot, and conversation. Before you start to write, plan out what you think could happen. Once you have decided what will happen, put your events in time order.

More than 275 years ago, Jonathan Swift wrote a story called *Gulliver's Travels*. In the book, he describes the fantastic adventures of Lemuel Gulliver. On one voyage, Gulliver travelled to Brobdingnag. The people in that country were enormous giants. Gulliver had some frightening experiences before he was finally able to escape.

Imagine that your friend accidentally spilled a magic liquid on you during a science class. Within a few seconds you were only five centimetres tall. What problems would you have?

Write a story telling about your adventures getting home from school.

_____

_____

_____

_____

_____

_____

_____

_____

_____

_____

Using Adjectives to Join Sentences

Adjectives usually come before the noun they tell about.

EXAMPLE: The **small** antelope walked down the **dusty** trail.

Sometimes adjectives come after the noun they describe.

EXAMPLE: The antelope's ears are **long** and **pointed**.

The adjectives from two sentences can often be joined with the word *and* to make a new sentence.

EXAMPLE: The trail was **narrow**. It was **slippery**. The trail was **narrow** and **slippery**.

Combine each of these pairs of sentences.

1. The weather is cold. The weather is wet.

   _____

2. The cat's fur was long. The car's fur was silky.

   _____

3. The bear's claws were curved. They also were sharp.

   _____

4. A snake's skin is dry. It is smooth, too.

   _____

5. My father is angry. He is upset as well.

   _____

EXERCISE 85 (Word Skills)
Onomatopoeia: The Sound Is the Meaning

Some words imitate sounds. The word *buzz* makes the sound of a fly. *Caw* copies the call of a crow. *Rattle* and *clank* describe the sounds of a heavy iron chain.

These words are called **onomatopoeia,** or **sound words**. When we hear them we think of the animal, person, or thing that makes that kind of sound.

A. Fill in the blanks in the following phrases with a sound word from the list below. Use your dictionary if you are unsure of the answer.

crackles	howls	ticks	twangs
drips	tinkles	whirs	wails

1. a clock _____   5. the electric motor _____

2. a small bell _____   6. a tap _____

3. a fire _____   7. a siren _____

4. a banjo _____   8. the wind _____

B. Here are ten words that describe the sounds made by birds and animals.

buzz	howl	hiss	moo	purr
quack	grunt	bark	gobble	baa

Write these sound words beside the correct bird or animal.

1. pigs _____   6. bees _____

2. ducks _____   7. dogs _____

3. sheep _____   8. cats _____

4. snakes _____   9. wolves _____

5. turkeys _____   10. cows _____

Onomatopoeia: The Sound Is the Meaning (continued)

C. Here are some words that can be used to describe the sounds people make.

giggle	sip	murmur	groan	grunt
whisper	slurp	snore	whistle	sigh

Write four interesting sentences. Use one or more of these words in each sentence.

_____

_____

_____

_____

_____

_____

_____

_____

D. Writers of comic strips often invent new words to help you hear strange sounds. The word *fzzzt,* for example, could describe the sputter of a burning fuse. What do you imagine when you hear the word *splat* or *zap?* Try to make an interesting new sound word to describe each of the following:

1. a bee and a mosquito colliding in mid-air _____

2. the rusty hinges on a door opening and closing _____

3. bubble gum bursting on the bubble maker's face _____

4. firecrackers exploding in a metal barrel _____

EXERCISE 86 (Paragraph Construction)
Using Picture-Making Adjectives

Did you know that English has more than 600 000 words? Many of these words are interesting adjectives. If you want to describe a tiger, for example, you could use adjectives like *powerful*, *savage*, and *fierce*. A lamb might be *timid*, *woolly*, or *playful*.

A. Circle the adjectives you would use to describe an elephant:

enormous, fearful, strong, tiny, gigantic, immense, powerful

B. Write four interesting adjectives that could describe a volcano.

_____

C. Sometimes we are lazy and we use adjectives such as *nice*, *fine*, and *good* too often. When you write, take time to think of exact, picture-making adjectives.

The writer of this paragraph has overused the adjective *nice*. Rewrite the paragraph. Whenever you come to the adjective *nice*, stop and think. Find an adjective that describes the noun more clearly. Use a different adjective each time.

Yesterday our class had a *nice* picnic. We travelled by bus to a *nice* park beside a *nice* lake. Our teacher had planned lots of *nice* races and games. For lunch we had a *nice* piece of watermelon. In the afternoon we had a *nice* swim in the lake.

_____

_____

_____

_____

_____

_____

Adverbs Tell How, Where, and When

Adverbs are words that tell us more about verbs. Their job is to make the meaning of the verb clear and exact. One way adverbs do this is by explaining *how* an action took place.

> EXAMPLE: *Garth climbed **rapidly** up the ladder.*
> *Garth climbed **cautiously** up the ladder.*

The words *rapidly* and *cautiously* are adverbs. They give us a clearer idea of how Garth climbed.

Adverbs can tell *where*.

> EXAMPLE: *Leave your boots **there**.*
> *The frightened mouse ran **outside**.*

Sometimes adverbs tell *when* something happened.

> EXAMPLE: *The fire started **yesterday**.*
> *The train arrived **early**.*

Circle all the verbs in these sentences. Then underline all the adverbs. Above each adverb, write whether it answers how, where, or when. The number in parentheses tells you how many adverbs are in each sentence.

EXAMPLE: The dog barked loudly. (1)

1. Rebecca slowly opened the window. (1)

2. Please leave the parcel downstairs. (1)

3. The three boys immediately ran inside. (2)

4. Ursula always walks quickly. (2)

5. The truck suddenly stopped. (1)

6. Yesterday Mario arrived early. (2)

7. Carefully and quickly, the boys crept forward. (3)

8. The stone landed here. (1)

EXERCISE 88 (Paragraph Construction)
Writing Exciting Descriptions

You have learned how to use adjectives and adverbs to make the meaning of your sentences clearer. You have practised choosing verbs that show action. You can use all those interesting words to write exciting descriptions.

A. Long ago people believed in dragons. They often told tales about these fantastic beasts. In the stories from Europe, the dragons were usually fierce and wicked. Chinese dragons, however, were quite different. The people of ancient China thought of them as kind, helpful creatures. Here is a description of a dragon. Do you think this beast lived in Europe or in China?

> Angrily out of the cave thundered a terrible dragon. The enormous monster was as tall as a four-storey building. Shiny, blackish-green scales covered its entire body. Each of its four massive legs ended in long bearlike claws. Just behind its forelegs grew two leathery wings like those of a gigantic bat. The dragon's huge head was truly frightening. Its mouth, which was large enough to swallow a ship in one gulp, was crammed with jagged, razor-sharp teeth. From the end of its enormous snout shot a fiery blast of flame and smoke.

1. Underline the topic sentence in this paragraph.

2. The word *terrible* in the topic sentence explains how the author feels about this dragon. List three details that prove that the dragon really was a terrible creature.

   a. _____

   b. _____

   c. _____

3. When you write a description, you must choose words that tell exactly what you saw. Write four interesting adjectives that help you see the dragon in your mind.

   _____

Writing Exciting Descriptions (continued)

B. Now it's your turn to try writing a description. Imagine that you are camping alone in the jungle. Early in the morning, you are awakened by an unusual sound. Crawling across the floor of the tent toward you is a strange insect. What does it look like? Is its body hairy or smooth? Is it striped, spotted, or all one colour? What words could you use to tell about its eyes, legs, and wings? How would you describe the sound it makes?

Start by listing six to eight details that explain why this insect is "strange."

1. _____

2. _____

3. _____

4. _____

5. _____

6. _____

7. _____

8. _____

In your notebook write a paragraph describing the insect. Be sure to use exact nouns, verbs, and adjectives to make your description clear. Here is a topic sentence for the paragraph.

Crawling slowly toward me was

the strangest insect I had ever seen.

EXERCISE 89 (Sentence Construction)
Adverbs Make the Meaning Clear

You can use adverbs to make the meaning of the verbs in your sentences more exact.

Read the following sentences about an old man walking down a sidewalk. How does the picture of the man change in your mind?

The old man walked **quickly** down the sidewalk.

The old man walked **cautiously** down the sidewalk.

The old man walked **proudly** down the sidewalk.

A. You can use adverbs to make the meaning of the verbs in your sentences more exact. Write an interesting adverb in each of the following blanks. Use a different adverb in each sentence.

1. They listened _____ to the fire chief's directions.

2. "Are you coming with us?" asked Jessie _____.

3. The crowd cheered _____ when Erin scored the goal.

4. The huge alligator slid _____ into the muddy water.

5. Rory _____ opened the strange package.

B. On the line below each question write several adverbs that would answer that question.

1. How would a mouse move across a meadow if a coyote were chasing it?

   _____

2. How would a mountain climber go up a steep cliff?

   _____

3. How would a group of young monkeys play?

   _____

EXERCISE 90 (Punctuation and Capitalization)
Apostrophes with Contractions

A **contraction** is two words shortened to make one word. The word *contract* means "to shrink" or "to make smaller." An apostrophe takes the place of the missing letter or letters.

> *EXAMPLE:* I + have = I've   she + is = she's   you + have = you've

Often contractions are used to join a verb with the word *not*. Usually you shorten *not* to *n't* and join it to the verb.

> *EXAMPLE:* does + not = doesn't   do + not = don't   have + not = haven't

There are two exceptions to this rule.

> *EXAMPLE:* can + not = can't   will + not = won't

Contractions are used to join a pronoun with forms of the verb *be*, *have*, *will*, and *would*. With these contractions, replace the first letter or letters of the verb with an apostrophe.

> *EXAMPLE:* I + am = I'm   he + had = he'd   they + would = they'd

UNIT 24

Rewrite each sentence. Use contractions whenever you can.

1. You have already been late three times.

   _____

2. Can you not see that I am busy?

   _____

3. "I would like to go," replied Jason, "but I can not."

   _____

4. Miss Garvin will not give us the doughnuts until we have paid for them.

   _____

   _____

EXERCISE 91 (Composition Construction)
Writing a Two-Paragraph Report

In a **report**, you give your reader information about a topic. Reports often have more than one paragraph.

Suppose you had to write a report about the black bear. You researched black bears in the library and found the following facts. On the line to the left of each sentence write **L** if the sentence explains what the bear looks like. Write **E** if it tells what it eats. Two of the sentences do not belong in either paragraph. Mark an **X** on the line beside these sentences.

_____ 1. They enjoy strawberries, blackberries, raspberries, and hazelnuts in the summer.

_____ 2. Black bears are easy to recognize.

_____ 3. Black bears get angry quickly.

_____ 4. In the autumn they feed on grasshoppers, acorns, wild grapes, and apples.

_____ 5. Adult black bears are about one metre tall.

_____ 6. They have short, strong legs and large feet.

_____ 7. A female bear usually has two cubs at the same time.

_____ 8. Although most black bears are black, some are reddish brown.

_____ 9. In the spring they eat spruce needles and the tender juicy stems of plants.

_____ 10. Black bears live on many different kinds of food.

Writing a Two-Paragraph Report (continued)

Now look at the sentences you marked with an **L**. Underline the one that would make the best topic sentence. Write this sentence on the line opposite Roman numeral I on the outline. Under this sentence list the three other items that describe what the black bear looks like. Be sure to put them in an order that makes sense.

Then underline the sentence that could be used as a topic sentence for a paragraph on what the black bear eats. Write this sentence on the line beside Roman numeral II. List all the sentences that talk about the black bear's eating habits. Use the seasons of the year to help you organize these sentences.

I. _____

   A. _____

     _____

   B. _____

     _____

   C. _____

     _____

II. _____

   A. _____

     _____

   B. _____

     _____

   C. _____

     _____

Adverbs: The -*ly* Clue

Most adjectives can be made into adverbs by adding the suffix -*ly*. If the adjective ends in *y*, change the *y* to *i* before adding -*ly* (*angry* – *angrily*).

Adjective	Adverb
a **slow** bus	The bus moved **slowly**.
the **noisy** monkeys	The monkeys chattered **noisily**.

Not all the words that end in -*ly* are adverbs. A few adjectives also end in -*ly*.

EXAMPLE: a **friendly** puppy   the **lovely** trail   a **weekly** paper

Some common adverbs such as *soon, inside, after, then,* and *well* do not end in -*ly*.

Circle the verb in each sentence. Then underline the adverbs. Remember that adverbs tell *when, where,* or *how* something happened. Pay close attention to words ending in -*ly*. The number in parentheses tells you how many adverbs there are in each sentence.

EXAMPLE: The huge locomotive moved slowly forward. (2)

1. Santella walked nervously across the stage. (1)

2. The lively kitten scampered quickly under the bed. (1)

3. Soon the moon shone brightly. (2)

4. The police officer opened the door cautiously. (1)

5. Usually the bus arrives here at eight o'clock. (2)

6. The injured trapper crawled painfully outside. (2)

7. Instantly the powerful eagle grabbed the rabbit. (1)

8. A family of raccoons wandered slowly along the lonely beach. (1)

9. Carefully they pushed the strange box inside. (2)

10. Yesterday, the telephone rang constantly. (2)

A. Punctuate these sentences correctly. Circle any letters that should be capitalized.

1. those puppies said greta are not for sale

2. youre coming with me replied mr powell

3. thats just not true shouted jessie

4. but why asked keith do you think we took the money

5. lunch wont be ready until 12:30 said aunt sue

B. Circle the adverb in each sentence. At the end of each sentence tell what question the adverb answers.

1. The young boy ran quickly across the bridge. _____

2. We must wash the car soon. _____ _____

3. My father parks his truck there. _____

4. The crowd cheered loudly when Sheryl scored the goal. _____

5. The bus from Camrose arrived fifteen minutes early. _____

C. Each word in boldface type is followed by four words. Circle the two words that are synonyms of the word in boldface type. Draw a line under the word that is the antonym. Draw an **X** through the word in each group that does not belong.

1. **true**	incorrect	right	like	correct
2. **dirty**	grimy	light	clean	filthy
3. **wet**	clean	damp	moist	dry
4. **beautiful**	pretty	ugly	bang	lovely

Review (continued)

D. Combine each pair of sentences.

1. A dolphin's skin is smooth. The dolphin's skin is rubbery.

   _____

2. A hippopotamus has long teeth. The teeth are curved as well.

   _____

3. Kangaroos have large hind legs. These hind legs are powerful.

   _____

E. Write the correct pronoun in the blank at the right.

1. Let's keep this a secret between you and (I, me). _____

2. Are you going with Judi and (he, him). _____

3. Francisco and (they, them) are going swimming. _____

4. Ms. Saunders paid Erik and (I, me) to cut her lawn. _____

5. Kameko and (she, her) are not here today. _____

F. Four of these sentences contain an error. Cross out the incorrect word and write your correction above it. Put a check mark in front of the correct sentence.

1. Yesterday the whether was cloudy and wet.

2. My younger sister has a lose tooth.

3. We had butter pecan ice cream for desert.

4. If you stand quite still, you may see the owl.

5. The geese are quiet noisy today.

Apostrophes Show Ownership

An apostrophe is used to show who owns, or **possesses**, something.

EXAMPLE: *the bulldozer belonging to Barry –* **Barry's** *bulldozer*

The noun *Barry's* tells us who owns the bulldozer. Nouns such as *Barry's* are called **possessive nouns**.

Here are the rules for using an apostrophe to show ownership or possession.

1. With singular nouns, add an apostrophe and *s*.

EXAMPLE: *The* **hawk's** *claws were long and curved.*

2. With plural nouns that end in *s*, add only an apostrophe.

EXAMPLE: *The* **boys'** *uniforms need cleaning.*

3. With plural nouns that end with a letter other than *s*, add an apostrophe and *s*.

EXAMPLE: *The* **men's** *boots were covered with mud.*

4 If two or more people own something together, only the last noun needs an apostrophe.

EXAMPLE: **Cindy and Sakina's** *cat won first prize*

Rewrite each group of words, using apostrophes where they are needed.

EXAMPLE: the stripes belonging to the zebra the zebra's stripes

1. the wheels of the boxcars _____

2. the shoes belonging to the women _____

3. the helicopter belonging to Pierre _____

4. the fur of the polar bear _____

5. the wings of the bees _____

6. the toys belonging to Dan and Kim _____

EXERCISE 94 (Composition Construction)
Persuasive Writing: Convince Me

Have you ever tried to change someone's mind? Perhaps you tried to persuade a friend to play baseball instead of football. Maybe you wanted your older brother to take you swimming. Often writers try to persuade people to do something. They may want you to buy a special pair of jeans or see a particular movie. When you write to persuade someone to do something you have to include reasons and you have to make what you want them to do sound interesting and appealing.

A. Here is a persuasive paragraph:

Jasper National Park is an exciting place to visit. Here you can enjoy horseback rides through spectacular wilderness. You can take gondola trips to the top of Whistler Mountain. Or you can go on breath-taking canoe expeditions down rushing mountain rivers. The fishing is superb. In the clear lakes and rivers you can catch Rocky Mountain whitefish and trout. More than 950 km of trails lead past thundering waterfalls and rugged mountains. During the summer, the meadows are covered with colourful wildflowers. In the campgrounds curious grey jays and ground squirrels visit. If you don't enjoy camping, the town of Jasper has modern stores, hotels, and motels. Jasper National Park is a perfect place for a vacation.

1. What does the writer of the paragraph hope people will do after reading it?

   _____

2. List four activities that someone visiting Jasper could do.

   _____

   _____

3. Find six descriptive adjectives the writer uses.

   _____

   _____

Persuasive Writing: Convince Me (continued)

B. Imagine that you own a lodge beside the lake in this photograph. Think of an interesting name for your lodge. Write it on the line below the photograph.

Now list five activities that people could do in this area.

_____

_____

_____

_____

_____ | _____

Then write a paragraph for a tourist brochure urging people to visit. Be sure you use picture-making adjectives. Remember that the topic sentence must catch the reader's attention.

_____

_____

_____

_____

_____

_____

_____

_____

EXERCISE 95 (Grammar and Usage)
Adverbs Move Easily

You have learned two ways to tell whether a word is an adverb.
1. Adverbs often tell more about verbs. They explain *how*, *when*, or *where* an action takes place.
2. Many adverbs end in *-ly*.

Adverbs are also very movable words. Often they can be moved from one spot to another without changing the meaning of the sentence.

> *EXAMPLE:* **Slowly** the ferry sailed into the harbour.
> The ferry sailed **slowly** into the harbour.
> The ferry sailed into the harbour **slowly**.

In these sentences the adverbs are printed in boldface type. Rewrite the sentences twice, putting the adverb in a different place each time.

EXAMPLE: Tina opened the door **cautiously**.

Cautiously, Tina opened the door.

Tina cautiously opened the door.

1. Erica **quickly** answered the question.

_____

_____

2. The detective examined the wallet **carefully**.

_____

_____

3. Alex **often** walks to school.

_____

_____

4. **Instantly** the gopher darted under the log.

_____

_____

EXERCISE 96 (Word Skills)
Understanding Abbreviations

An **abbreviation** is a shortened form of a word.

> EXAMPLE: Doctor – Dr.   November – Nov.   Friday – Fri.

Most abbreviations end with a period. The metric symbols, however, do not have periods.

> EXAMPLE: metre – m   gram – g   litre – L

A. Write the word or words that each of these abbreviations stands for. Use your dictionary to check your words.

EXAMPLE: NHL <u>National Hockey League</u>

1. St. _____
2. km _____
3. N.L. _____
4. Oct. _____
5. P.S. _____

6. Mon. _____
7. B.C. _____
8. Mr. _____
9. Jan. _____
10. UN _____

UNIT 26

B. Rewrite these groups of words using abbreviations.

1. Doctor Bell _____
2. September 9 _____
3. Mister Chen _____
4. December 28 _____
5. physical education _____
6. seven kilograms _____
7. thirty litres _____
8. Prince Edward Island _____

EXERCISE 97 (Grammar and Usage)
Using Adjectives to Compare

Are there any tall structures in your community? There are many tall buildings in Canada. Read these sentences carefully.

The Royal Bank Tower in Vancouver is **tall**.

The Calgary Tower is **taller** than the Royal Bank Tower.

The CN Tower in Toronto is the **tallest** free-standing tower in the world.

When you explain how things are alike or different, you are making **comparisons**. If you compare two people or things, add the suffix *-er* to the adjective. If you compare more than two people or things, add the suffix *-est* to the adjective.

Sometimes the spelling of the adjective changes when *-er* or *-est* is added.

1. If the adjective ends in *e*, drop the *e* before adding *-er* or *-est*.

   large   larger   largest
   wise   wiser   wisest

2. If the adjective ends in *y*, change the *y* to *i* and add *-er* or *-est*.

   heavy   heavier   heaviest
   pretty   prettier   prettiest

3. If an adjective has only one vowel and ends in a single consonant, double the consonant before adding *-er* or *-est*.

   wet   wetter   wettest
   hot   hotter   hottest

Using Adjectives to Compare (continued)

A. Beside each of these adjectives write its -er and -est forms.

Adjective	To compare two (-er)	To compare three or more (-est)
1. fine	_____	_____
2. big	_____	_____
3. small	_____	_____
4. happy	_____	_____
5. thin	_____	_____
6. deep	_____	_____

B. Fill in the blank in each sentence with the correct form of the adjective in parentheses. Be ready to explain the reason for your choice.

UNIT
26

1. February is the _____ (short) month of the year.

2. Last night it was _____ (cold) in Toronto than in Winnipeg.

3. That elephant is the _____ (big) animal in the zoo.

4. Paulo is the _____ (fast) player on the hockey team.

5. Glass is hard, but diamonds are _____ (hard).

6. The _____ (hot) day of the year was July 25.

7. Scott is the _____ (old) of the two boys.

8. Our _____ (rainy) month is usually November.

9. Who is _____ (tall), Rosalie or Sabina?

10. Blake is the _____ (young) player in the school band.

EXERCISE 98 (Sentence Construction)
Adding Interest by Expanding Sentences

You can make sentences more interesting by expanding them with more information or more description. Here are three ways you can do that.

    1. Add an adjective that describes the noun.

    2. Add an adverb that makes the meaning of the verb clearer.

    3. Add a group of words, such as *on the lake* or *in the crowded restaurant*, that tells where the action took place.

A. Expand each of these sentences.

EXAMPLE: The eagle flew.   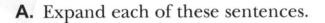 The huge eagle flew swiftly to the top of a tall tree.

    1. The man jumped.

       _____

    2. The horses trotted.

       _____

    3. The airplane crashed.

       _____

    4. The robber disappeared.

       _____

B. Now rewrite two of your sentences putting the adverb in a different place.

_____

_____

_____

_____

Explaining with Similes

When you explain how things are alike or different, you are making comparisons. A comparison that uses the word *like* or *as* is called a **simile**. A simile describes something by comparing it to something else.

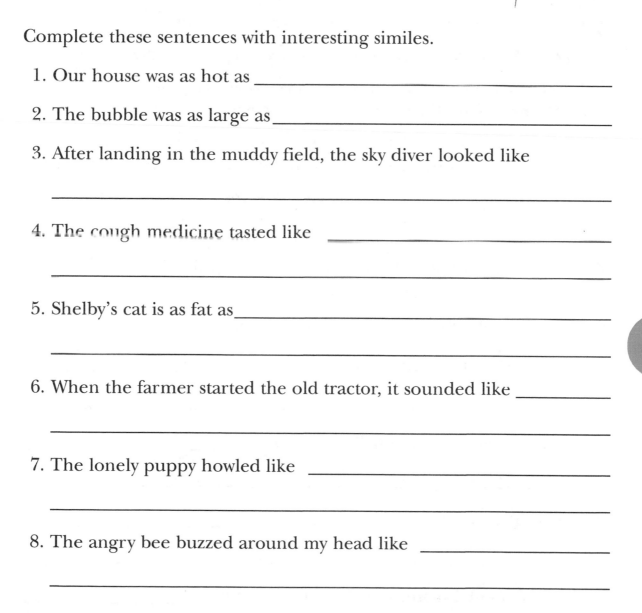

EXAMPLE: *The icicles sparkle like diamonds.*
My hands are as cold as ice.

Complete these sentences with interesting similes.

1. Our house was as hot as _____

2. The bubble was as large as _____

3. After landing in the muddy field, the sky diver looked like

   _____

4. The cough medicine tasted like _____

   _____

5. Shelby's cat is as fat as _____

   _____

6. When the farmer started the old tractor, it sounded like _____

   _____

7. The lonely puppy howled like _____

   _____

8. The angry bee buzzed around my head like _____

   _____

UNIT 27

EXERCISE 100 (Sentence Construction)

Linking Ideas with Compound Sentences

The words *and, but,* and *or* are often used to join ideas. These words are called **conjunctions**. Conjunctions always join words that are used in the same way.

> *EXAMPLE: Polar bears eat seals **and** fish.*

The conjunction *and* joins the nouns *seals* and *fish.*

> *EXAMPLE: The polar bear's head is long **and** narrow.*

The conjunction *and* joins the adjectives *long* and *narrow.*

> *EXAMPLE: Slowly **and** carefully the polar bear crept across the ice.*

The conjunction *and* joins the adverbs *slowly* and *carefully.*
Sometimes conjunctions are used to join complete sentences.

> *EXAMPLE: The polar bear's fur is white. Its claws and tongue are black.*
> *The polar bear's fur is white, but its claws and tongue are black.*

A sentence made up of two complete sentences is called a **compound sentence**. Notice that a comma is used in front of the conjunction.

Make these sentences into compound sentences. Be sure that the words you add are complete sentences.

EXAMPLE: Curt waited for two hours, but ___the bus did not arrive.___

1. Yasin washed the dishes, and _____

_____

2. Lisa is going to the football game, but _____

_____

3. Turn the hose off, or _____

_____

4. The frightened man raced for the door, but _____

_____

More Practice Writing Stories

Sometimes when you write a story, you can imagine you are someone else—or even an animal or alien or fairy-tale creature. You have to put yourself in that person's place and imagine what they would experience, what they would see, hear, smell, feel, and say.

Canada geese are huge water birds. Their strong wings can carry them long distances. The geese also use their wings in fights to pound their enemies.

Canada geese like to live near lakes, ponds, streams, and marshes. These birds eat grasshoppers and other insects. They also feed on grass, grain, and the leaves and roots of water plants.

Every autumn large flocks of Canada geese fly south to northern Mexico. Usually several families travel together. A large flock may contain more than a hundred birds. They usually travel in a V formation and honk as they fly.

Imagine that you are a member of a flock of Canada geese. One foggy night you become separated from the rest of the group. What problems might you have? What animals would you have to watch out for? How might your experience end?

In your notebook write a story about your adventures as a lost goose. Use the following sentence as a beginning. When you finish writing, edit your story. Start new paragraphs where necessary. Leave out any sentences that do not belong. Be sure that you have used exact words so that your reader will know how you felt.

Suddenly, I realized I was alone.

UNIT
27

It's or *Its*?

Be careful not to confuse the words *it's* and *its*. Remember that *it's* is short for *it is* or *it has*.

EXAMPLE: **It's** your turn.
It's been raining all day.

The word *its* means "belonging to it."

EXAMPLE: The dog buried **its** bone.

A. Circle the correct word in each of the following sentences.

1. (It's, Its) Chico's idea.

2. The cat chased (it's, its) tail.

3. Don't you think (it's, its) time to leave?

4. Did you fill (it's, its) dish with water?

5. (It's, Its) very hot in this room.

6. (It's, Its) interesting to watch a raccoon wash (it's, its) food.

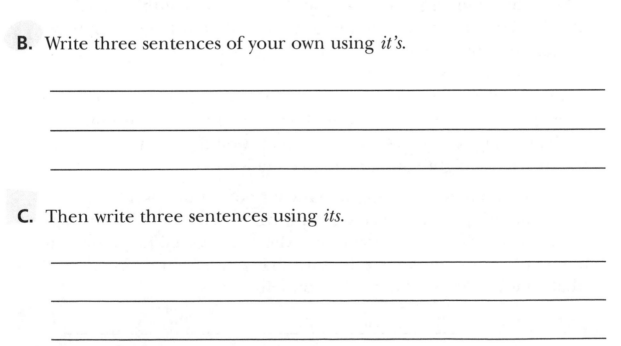

B. Write three sentences of your own using *it's*.

_____

_____

_____

C. Then write three sentences using *its*.

_____

_____

_____

EXERCISE 103 (Punctuation and Capitalization)
Apostrophes with Pronouns and Contractions

Pronouns, like nouns, can be used to show possession, or ownership. **Possessive pronouns** show who something belongs to. They do *not* use an apostrophe.

> EXAMPLE: whose   *Whose gloves are these?*
> your   *Your mother is here.*

Contractions are two words shortened into one. An apostrophe is used in place of the letter or letters that have been left out.

> EXAMPLE: who's   *who has, who is*
> you're   *you are*

A. Circle the correct word in each sentence.

1. I know (you're, your) anxious to open (you're, your) presents.

2. (Who's, Whose) coat was left in (you're, your) mother's car?

3. (You're, Your) going to have to leave early if (you're, your) going to be on time.

4. (Who's, Whose) got the key to (you're, your) lock?

5. Do you know (who's, whose) dog dug the hole under (you're, your) fence?

B. Write sentences of your own using the following words correctly.

1. who's _____

2. whose _____

3. you're _____

4. your _____

UNIT
28

EXERCISE 104 (Sentence Construction)
Joining Sentences with *and*, *but*, and *or*

The **conjunctions** *and*, *but*, and *or* have very specific uses.

1. Use **and** when the second sentence gives added information.

EXAMPLE: *Finally the whistle blew,* **and** *the boat moved away from the dock.*

2. Use **but** when the second sentence tells an opposite or different idea.

EXAMPLE: *A frog's skin is smooth and moist,* **but** *a toad's skin is dry and rough.*

3. Use **or** when the second sentence gives a choice.

EXAMPLE: *The fence must be fixed,* **or** *the horses will escape.*

Join the following pairs of simple sentences with *or, but,* or *and*. Be sure to punctuate each sentence correctly.

1. Suddenly we heard a loud bang. All the lights went out.

_____

_____

2. Latoya was tall. Her father was short.

_____

_____

3. Speak louder. People will not hear you.

_____

_____

4. About noon the river started to rise. The police told everyone to leave.

_____

_____

More Practice with Synonyms

A synonym is a word that means the same or nearly the same as another word. Some synonyms have almost exactly the same meaning. Can you see any difference in meaning between *wealthy* and *rich*? There is a difference between *hungry* and *starved*.

A. How do the words in each of the following synonym pairs differ in meaning? For each word pair, write two sentences that show how the meanings are different. Use your dictionary if you are not sure what the words mean.

EXAMPLE: walk, march

Would you like to walk to school with me?

The band played, and the soldiers marched down the street

1. cool and bitter _____

   _____

2. loud and shrill _____

   _____

3. cut and tear _____

   _____

4. angry and enraged _____

   _____

UNIT 28

B. Work with a classmate. Imagine that your new bicycle has disappeared. The police would like an exact description of what it looks like. Be sure to use exact adjectives to write a description of your bicycle. Use a thesaurus to help you find the right words.

EXERCISE 106 (Word Skills)
Synonym Word Search

Remember that synonyms are words that have the same meaning or a similar meaning.

Each word listed on this page has a synonym hidden in the word search puzzle. Circle the words in the puzzle. Then write each word in the blank beside its synonym.

```
S  T  U  D  E  N  T  L  N  S
M  I  W  I  S  E  S  E  E  H
A  N  E  F  A  S  T  A  W  I
S  Y  T  F  B  K  R  P  O  P
H  I  T  I  O  I  E  B  E  H
R  U  G  C  V  N  E  I  V  U
M  A  D  U  E  N  T  G  I  R
C  H  I  L  L  Y  E  L  L  R
N  E  A  T  P  R  E  T  T  Y
D  I  N  N  E  R  T  E  L  L
```

10. mat _____

11. road _____

12. thin _____

13. smart _____

14. lovely _____

15. rush _____

16. look _____

17. shout _____

1. break _____

2. small _____

3. pupil _____

4. strike _____

5. hard _____

6. tidy _____

7. quick _____

8. over _____

9. angry _____

18. cold _____

19. boat _____

20. bad _____

21. jump _____

22. large _____

23. modern _____

24. damp _____

25. say _____

26. supper _____

EXERCISE 107 (Word Skills)
Antonym Crossword

Remember that antonyms are words that mean the opposite of each other.

Fill in the crossword with antonyms for the clues given.

Across

1 thick	18 empty
4 narrow	20 open
9 out	21 strong
11 early	24 huge
13 wild	25 foolish
14 he	27 less
15 tiny	29 seldom
17 take	30 day

Down

2 low	14 dangerous
3 yes	15 find
4 unwrap	16 high
5 live	19 arrive
6 dull	20 stormy
7 sour	22 queen
8 sad	23 east
10 buy	26 come
12 short	28 off

UNIT 29

Learning About *Good* and *Well*

Do you have trouble with *good* and *well*? Here is what you should know about these words.

    1. **Well** may be used as an adverb to tell *how* something is done.

*EXAMPLE: The team from Mississauga played **well** last night.*

    2. **Well** may also be used as an adjective to mean "in good health."

*EXAMPLE: After supper Pamela didn't feel **well**.*

    3. **Good** is usually an adjective. It should never be used as an adverb.

*EXAMPLE: Yesterday was a **good** day to climb the mountain.*

Fill in each blank using *good* or *well* correctly.

1. Devin can't see very _____ without his glasses.

2. Marissa is a _____ athlete.

3. Do you feel _____ enough to go to the birthday party?

4. Did you have a _____ time at Lake Simcoe?

5. How _____ can you swim?

6. Melina didn't feel _____ on Wednesday.

7. Jacques sings _____ and is also a _____ violinist.

8. The cake your sister made tastes _____.

9. Be sure to mix the paint _____.

10. Kaylee can certainly ski _____.

11. Logan is a _____ snowboarder.

12. Perlita rode the horse _____.

13. I am feeling _____ today.

14. The goalie really played _____ in last night's game.

EXERCISE 109 (Grammar and Usage)
There, Their, and They're

There means "in that place."

    EXAMPLE: *Leave your shoes* **there**.

Their means "belonging to them."

    EXAMPLE: **Their** *horse won first prize.*

They're is a short form, or contraction, of "they are."

    EXAMPLE: **They're** *always late.*

Write *there*, *their*, or *they're* in each blank to complete the sentence correctly.

1. _____ planning to leave as soon as _____ suitcases are packed.

2. _____ car was parked right _____.

3. _____ going to visit _____ relatives in Labrador.

4. _____ coming with _____ cousins.

5. We will be _____ on Wednesday.

6. _____ planning to surprise _____ parents.

7. They stayed _____ until _____ plane arrived.

8. Please hang _____ jackets.

9. _____ cat always sleeps _____.

10. If _____ not home by nine o'clock, _____ mother will be upset.

EXERCISE 110 (Sentence Construction)
More Practice with Combining Sentences

In this book you have learned four ways to join sentences.

1. Use a compound subject.

EXAMPLE: *Grizzly bears hunt bighorn sheep. Wolves hunt them, too.*

Grizzly bears and wolves hunt bighorn sheep.

2. Use a compound predicate.

EXAMPLE: *The male bighorn raised his head. He sniffed the breeze.*

The male bighorn raised his head and sniffed the breeze.

3. Use the adjectives from two sentences in a new sentence.

EXAMPLE: *The bighorn's ears are short. They are also pointed.*

The bighorn's ears are short and pointed.

4. Use a compound sentence.

EXAMPLE: *The lambs played in the meadow. Their mothers watched for enemies.*

The lambs played in the meadow, but their mothers watched for enemies.

More Practice with Combining Sentences (continued)

The following paragraphs are full of short sentences. Rewrite the paragraphs joining sentences together whenever you can.

    The bighorn sheep that live in northern British Columbia, the Yukon, and Alaska are called Dall sheep. During the winter their hair is long. It is also thick. It is pure white. Their horns are yellowish-brown. Their hooves are the same colour. In the summer they eat grass. In the winter they eat the tender shoots of shrubs.

    Their lambs are born in May and June. Usually the mothers have only one baby. Sometimes they have twins. The lambs' coats are soft. They are woolly, too. At first the mothers nurse them. Before long they start to nibble grass.

_____

_____

_____

_____

_____

_____

_____

_____

_____

_____

_____

EXERCISE 111 (Composition Construction)
More Practice with Sentence Variety

Here are two ways to improve a paragraph.
1. Join sentences if you can. Do not, however, just string sentences together with *and*. (Review the suggestions for combining sentences in Exercise 110.)
2. Try not to have sentences that follow each other start with the same subject.

Here are two paragraphs from a report about lizards.

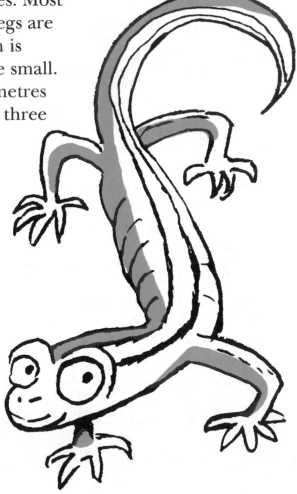

Lizards are very interesting reptiles. Most lizards move on four legs. Their legs are short. Their skin is dry. Their skin is covered with scales. The scales are small. Many lizards are only a few centimetres long. Some lizards are more than three hundred centimetres long.

Small lizards eat insects. They eat spiders, too. They catch them with their tongues. Their tongues are long and sticky. A few lizards live only on plants. The larger lizards catch wild pigs and deer. They also catch birds. Most lizards do not drink water. They live by sucking dew from flat stones and leaves.

The writer of these paragraphs used too many short sentences. Rewrite these paragraphs in your notebook using the rules at the top of this page.

A. Write a contraction for each group of words. Be sure to put the apostrophe in the right place.

1. have not _____   5. do not _____

2. she will _____   6. they are _____

3. can not _____   7. will not _____

4. he would _____   8. he has _____

B. Choose the correct word in each of the following sentences, and write it in the blank.

1. Was (your, you're) sister hurt? _____

2. (They're, Their) coming with Emily. _____

3. (Whose, Who's) jacket is this? _____

4. (It's, Its) going to rain today. _____

5. (Who's, Whose) going with Ted? _____

6. Is (it's, its) leg broken? _____

C. Fill in each blank using *good* or *well* correctly.

1. Mandy rode the horse _____.

2. Zev is a _____ soccer player.

3. How _____ can you ice skate?

4. My mother's fresh baked bread always smells _____.

5. Anna did not feel _____ after the hockey game.

6. Both Colin and Christopher play the violin _____.

UNITS
25–29

Review (continued)

D. Fill in the blank in each of these sentences with the correct form of the adjective in parentheses. Be ready to explain the reasons for your choice.

1. Tim is the _____ (tall) of the twins.

2. Nicole is the _____ (young) girl in our class.

3. Our school is the _____ (old) in our province.

4. The _____ (small) of the nine planets is Pluto.

E. Join each pair of sentences to make one strong compound sentence.

1. The weather is cold. The weather is also clear.

   _____

2. Miguel collects stamps. Duncan collects coins.

   _____

3. My mother's pies are good. Aunt Rachel's are even better.

   _____

F. Write *there, their,* or *they're* in each blank to complete the sentence correctly.

1. In _____ game at two o'clock _____ playing the team from Hull.

2. Just put _____ uniforms _____.

3. _____ going to visit _____ friends in Saskatchewan.

4. Please send me _____ address in Nova Scotia.

5. They left _____ hockey sticks right _____.

MINI-THESAURUS

afraid   anxious, cowardly, horrified, fearful, frightened, nervous, scared, terrified, troubled, uneasy

angry   annoyed, aroused, cross, enraged, furious, in a rage, inflamed, infuriated, irate, peeved

ask   demand, inquire, question, quiz, request

bad   awful, evil, horrible, naughty, rotten, spoiled, unfavourable, unpleasant, wicked, wrong

beautiful   attractive, charming, dazzling, desirable, elegant, gorgeous, handsome, lovely, magnificent, pretty, sparkling, splendid, stunning

begin   commence, inaugurate, launch, start

big   colossal, enormous, gigantic, great, huge, immense, jumbo, large, mammoth, massive, titanic, vast

brave   bold, courageous, daring, fearless, gallant, heroic, unafraid, valiant

break   burst, crack, crush, damage, destroy, shatter, smash, split, wreck

bright   brilliant, colourful, dazzling, gleaming, glittering, glowing, shimmering, shiny, sparkling

call   bellow, cry, roar, scream, whisper, yell

catch   capture, grab, hook, rope, snare, snatch

cool   bitter, chilly, cold, freezing, frigid, frosty, ice cold, icy, unheated, wintry

cry   bawl, bellow, exclaim, howl, roar, scream, shout, sob, wail, weep, yell

cut   carve, chop, clip, saw, slash, slice, snip

dark   black, dim, dismal, dreary, gloomy, murky, shadowy, sunless

delicious   appetizing, enjoyable, juicy, luscious, scrumptious, succulent, tasty

dirty   dingy, dusty, filthy, grimy, messy, smudged, soiled, unwashed

dull   boring, dreary, humdrum, tedious, tiring, uninteresting

eat   bite, chew, crunch, devour, feast on, gobble, gnaw, graze, grind, gulp, munch, nibble, swallow

fall	collapse, dive, drop, plunge, sink, topple, tumble
fast	fleet, hasty, prompt, quick, rapid, speedy, swift
fat	chubby, obese, overweight, plump, pudgy, stout
full	crammed, crowded, heaping, jammed, loaded, overflowing, packed, stuffed
get	acquire, collect, earn, find, gather, obtain
good	agreeable, excellent, fine, first-rate, marvellous, pleasant, reliable, satisfactory, splendid, superb, superior, well-behaved, wonderful, trustworthy
happy	cheerful, contented, delighted, glad, jolly, joyful, jubilant, merry, overjoyed, pleased, satisfied.
hate	abhor, despise, detest, disapprove, dislike, loathe
hit	collide, crash into, pound, punch, run into, slam into, smash into, strike
hot	baked, boiling, burning, fiery, roasting, scalded, scorched, sizzling, steaming, sunny, tropical, warm
hurry	accelerate, bustle, dash, dart, flash, hasten, hustle, race, run, rush, speed, zip, zoom
important	essential, famous, indispensable, influential, necessary, outstanding, prominent, significant, substantial, valuable, well-known
interesting	absorbing, appealing, amusing, arousing, attractive, engrossing, entertaining, enthralling, exciting, fascinating, gripping, intriguing, spellbinding, thrilling
kind	considerate, friendly, generous, gentle, helpful, pleasant, thoughtful, warm-hearted
little	dwarfish, miniature, minute, pigmy, small, tiny, wee
look	explore, gape, hawk, glance, glare, glimpse, hunt, inspect, observe, peek, peep, peer, search for, stare, study, watch
mad	angry, annoyed, cross, disagreeable, enraged, furious, raging
make	assemble, build, construct, create, develop, fashion, invent, manufacture, produce
move	amble, bound, climb, crawl, creep, dart, dash, gallop, hobble, jog, paddle, race, ride, run, rush, saunter, scamper, scramble, scurry, shuffle, slide, slither, stagger, streak, stride, swagger, tear, toddle, trot, waddle, walk

new	current, modern, recent, unused
old	aged, ancient, antique, elderly, feeble
right	accurate, correct, exact, perfect, true
sad	dejected, depressed, gloomy, miserable, sorrowful, sorry, unhappy
say	admit, announce, argue, assert, boast, chat, claim, comment, complain, continue, discuss, explain, express, grumble, growl, insist, mention, mumble, mutter, note, order, promise, recall, remark, reply, snap, suggest, thunder, urge, whisper, yell
show	demonstrate, disclose, explain, guide, point out, teach
slowly	gradually, lazily, leisurely, sluggishly, unhurriedly
smart	bright, brilliant, clever, intellectual, intelligent, wise
stop	block, cease, conclude, discontinue, end, halt, prevent
strange	astonishing, extraordinary, fantastic, odd, peculiar, queer, unusual, weird
strong	forceful, mighty, muscular, powerful, rugged, sturdy, tough
take	capture, carry off, grab, kidnap, obtain, pick up, seize, snap up, snatch
thin	lean, scrawny, skinny, slender, slim
true	accurate, actual, authentic, correct, exact, genuine, real, right
ugly	hideous, repulsive, unattractive, unsightly
unhappy	cheerless, dejected, depressed, discontented, discouraged, gloomy, heart-broken, miserable, sad, sorrowful
walk	file, hike, limp, march, pace, prance, stagger, stalk, stamp, stride, stroll, strut, stumble, tiptoe, trudge, waddle
wet	damp, drenched, humid, moist, rainy, soaked, soggy, sodden, watery
wonderful	amazing, delightful, enjoyable, fabulous, fantastic, marvellous, spectacular, superb
worried	agitated, anxious, concerned, disturbed, troubled, upset
wrong	false, inaccurate, incorrect, unsuitable, untrue

INDEX

Abbreviations, 117
Accent marks, 24
Addresses, commas and, 34
Adjectives, 96, 97, 99, 102, 104, 118, 136
Adverbs, 103, 104, 106, 110, 111, 116
Alphabetical order, 8, 12
Animal words, 25
Antonyms, 57, 64, 68, 82, 111, 129
Apostrophes, 107, 111, 113, 125

Base words, 61, 80
Body, of letter, 70

Capitalization
    buildings, 14
    holidays, 9
    languages, 14
    nationalities, 14
    organizations, 14
    place names, 9
    proper nouns, 7
    of quotations, 65, 73
    review, 27, 81, 111
    sentences, 2
    titles, 14
Climax, of story, 90
Closing, of letter, 70
Commas
    with addresses, 34
    with dates, 29
    in direct address, 39
    with quotations, 62, 65, 73
    review, 55
    with series, 45
Comparatives, 118, 136
Compounds
    predicates, 35, 83
    review, 82
    sentences, 38, 63, 122
    subjects, 35, 83
    words, 35
Confusing words, 88
Conjunctions, 122, 126
Contractions, 107, 111, 135
Conversations, writing, 93, 98

Definitions, in dictionary, 22
Descriptions, 104
Detail sentences, 26, 37, 48
Dialogue. see Conversations
Dictionary usage, 8, 13, 17, 22, 27, 30, 40
Direct address, commas and, 39
Directions, following and giving, 50

Editing, 20, 26
Entry words, 8

Examples, 22, 52
Exclamation marks, 29, 72
Exclamations, 10

Good and *well*, 130, 135
Guide words, 17, 27

Heading, of letter, 70
Homonyms, 51, 87

Imperatives, 10
It's or *its*, 124, 135

Letters, friendly, 70

Main idea, 16, 26, 37

Nouns
    agreement with verbs, 41, 46
    common, 6
    definition, 4
    plural, 15, 18, 41, 46
    pronouns and, 66
    proper, 6, 7, 14
    review, 27, 28, 55
    singular, 15, 18, 41, 46

Onomatopoeia, 100
Order, 42, 43, 48

Paragraphs
    definition, 16
    detail sentences, 26, 37, 48
    explanatory, 48, 52, 60
    main ideas, 16, 26, 37
    order, 42, 48
    topic sentences, 19, 20, 26, 37
    unity, 16, 26, 37
Past participles, 31, 44, 54, 56, 59
Periods, usage, 29
Persuasive writing, 114
Plot, 90, 92, 98
Possessives, 113
Postcards, 76
Predicates, 32, 35, 41, 46, 55
Prefixes, 61, 68, 80
Prepositions, 84
Pronouns, 67
    agreement with nouns, 69
    definition, 66
    object, 78, 79, 84, 85
    with prepositions, 84
    review, 81, 82, 112
    subject, 75, 78, 85
Pronunciation keys, 30

Question marks, 29, 72
Questions, 10, 86
Quotation marks, 62, 65, 72, 81
Quotations, 62, 65, 72, 73, 81, 86, 111

Reasons, explaining with, 60
Reports, 108

Salutation, 70
Sentences
    combining, 38, 83, 126, 132
    complete, 3
    compound, 38, 63
    definition, 2
    expanding, 120
    incomplete, 3
    patterns, 74, 77
    predicates, 32
    review, 28, 82, 112
    run-on, 5
    subjects, 32
    topic, 19, 20
    types of, 10
    variety, 134
Signature, 70
Similar words, 88, 112
Similes, 121
Statements, 10
Story construction, 89, 90, 92, 98, 123
Stress marks, 24
Subjects, 32, 35, 41, 46, 55, 74, 77
Suffixes, 80
Syllables, 24
Synonyms, 33, 82, 111, 127, 128

Tenses, 36, 44, 54, 56, 59
There is and *There are*, 46
There, Their, and *They're*, 131, 135, 136
Thesaurus, use of, 58, 93
Time order, 89, 92, 98
Topic sentences, 19, 20, 26, 37
Two, Too, and *To*, 47

Uppercase. *see* Capitalization

Verbs
    adverbs and, 103
    agreement with nouns, 41, 46
    choosing, 58, 104
    definition, 21
    forms of *to be*, 21
    helping, 31
    irregular, 44, 54, 59
    past participles and, 31, 44, 54, 59
    regular, 36
    review, 55, 56
    tense, 36, 44, 54, 59

Well and *good*, 130
    review, 135
Words, scrambled, 1

PHYSICAL SCIENCE

Matter and Motion

Science Action Labs

Written by Edward Shevick

Illustrated by Marguerite Jones

Teaching & Learning Company

1204 Buchanan St., P.O. Box 10

Carthage, IL 62321-0010

This book belongs to

_____

Cover by Marguerite Jones

Copyright © 1998, Teaching & Learning Company

ISBN No. 1-57310-144-3

Printing No. 987654321

Teaching & Learning Company
1204 Buchanan St., P.O. Box 10
Carthage, IL 62321-0010

Table of Contents
Science Action Labs

1: Fun with Physical Science 5

2: What's the Matter? 8

3: The Characteristics of Matter 12

4: Superball Olympics 15

5: Egg Matter: A Packaging Contest 17

6: Spring Lab: Experimenting with Elastic Matter 18

7: Mousetrap Science 22

8: Friction: Friend or Foe? 23

9: Spoolmobile Contest: Overcoming Friction 27

10: Periodic Table Lab 29

11: Puzzling Atoms 33

12: Edible Atoms 34

13: Inertia: Newton's First Law of Motion 36

14: Newton's Second Law of Motion 39

15: Action and Reaction: Newton's Third Law of Motion 43

16: Newton's Action Reaction Puzzler 46

17: Momentum Lab: Transferring the Energy of Motion 47

18: Momentum Challenge: Geo Versus Cadillac 50

19: Pendulums in Motion 52

20: Time Lab: Making Your Own Pendulum Clock 54

21: The Tower of Pisa Puzzler 57

22: Newton's Falling Apple 59

23: Falling Fun 62

Answer Key 64

Dear Teacher or Parent,

The spirit of Sir Isaac Newton will be with you and your students in this book about **matter** and **motion**. Newton loved science, math and experimenting. He explained the laws of gravity. He demonstrated the nature of light. He discovered how planets stay in orbit around our sun.

Physical Science can help your students in many ways. Choose some activities to spice up your class demonstrations. Some sections can be converted to hands-on lab activities for the entire class. Some can be developed into student projects or reports. Every class has a few students with a special zest for science. Encourage them to pursue some experiments on their own.

Enjoy these science activities as much as Newton would have. They are designed to make your students **think**. Thinking and solving problems are what science is all about. Each section encourages thought. Students are often asked to come up with their best and most reasonable guess as to what will happen. Scientists call this type of guess a **hypothesis**. They are told how to assemble the materials necessary to actually try out each activity. Scientists call this **experimenting**.

Don't expect the experiments to always prove the hypothesis right. These physical science activities have been picked to challenge students' thinking abilities.

All the activities in **Physical Science** are based upon science principles. Many are explained by Newton's laws. That is why Sir Isaac Newton has been used as a guide through the pages of this book. Newton will help your students think about, build and experiment with these activities. Newton will be with them in every activity to advise, encourage and praise their efforts.

The answers you will need are on page 64. You will also find some science facts that will help your students understand what happened.

Here are some suggestions to help your students succeed:

1. **Observe carefully.**
2. **Follow directions.**
3. **Measure carefully.**
4. **Hypothesize intelligently.**
5. **Experiment safely.**
6. **Keep experimenting until you succeed.**

Sincerely,

Ed

Edward Shevick

Fun with Physical Science

Two Great Physical Scientists

The study of matter, motion and energy is called **physics**. Scientists who study these subjects are called physicists. Here is some background on two of the world's greatest physicists.

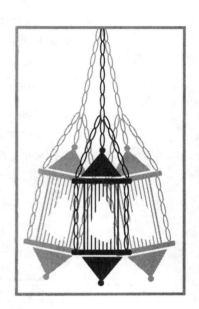

Galileo Galilei was born in Pisa, Italy, in 1564. Before his death in 1642, he made many discoveries about astronomy and the physics of falling objects. As a child, Galileo showed unusual skill in making toys. He became an accomplished musician and printer. Galileo studied both philosophy and medicine in college.

Galileo was only 20 when he discovered the law of the pendulum. He used his pulse to time the swing of lamps in the Pisa Cathedral. Supposedly he dropped different size cannonballs from Pisa's Leaning Tower in his experiments about gravity.

Galileo improved the telescope and became convinced that the Earth was not the center of the universe. He was punished for teaching what he knew was right.

Sir Isaac Newton was born in England in 1642 and died in 1727. After receiving his degree at Cambridge University, he went home to study and think. In less than 18 months at home, this very young man discovered laws of light, color, motion and gravity. Newton will be your guide to help you study physics in this book.

If I have seen further in physics, it is from standing on the shoulders of giants.

–Sir Isaac Newton

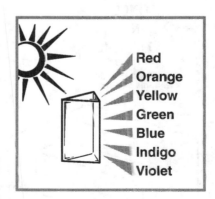

Red
Orange
Yellow
Green
Blue
Indigo
Violet

Name _____

Newton's Favorite Scientific Fairy Tale

Newton likes to tell the imaginary story of a tiny green "thing" that landed on Earth one day from outer space. It was soft, shapeless and completely motionless. It had none of the characteristics of life as we know it on Earth. Scientists poked it and examined it. They did countless experiments but could learn nothing about its nature or whether it was really alive. The green blob just sat there without moving or reacting in any way.

Finally one brilliant scientist sat down next to the green "thing" and asked how it felt, how it liked being on Earth and what it thought about the weather. The green "thing" began to talk and answer all sorts of questions.

The lesson to be learned from our mysterious green friend is simple. If you want to learn something, you must ask the **right questions**. Physicists are skilled at asking the right questions of nature.

Physicists Observe Carefully

Newton has picked optical illusions to help you improve your observation powers. Study them carefully.

ONCE
IN A
A LIFETIME

What's wrong with this sentence?

Can you see TWO faces?

Is the dot at the front or back of the cube?

Stare at these steps. They can change direction.

Which boy is the tallest?

6

Name _____

Newton's Math Challenge

Physics and math are as closely related as two brothers. To be a physicist, you must also be a mathematician. Here are two of Newton's favorite math problems.

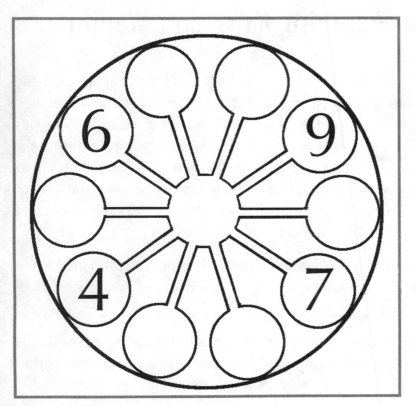

Circular Math

Use the numbers from 1 through 11 to fill in all the circles. Each line must add up to the **same** total. Newton is giving you two lines to get you started.

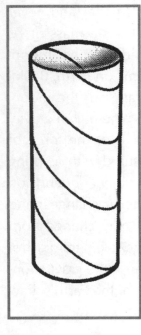

The Unfolded Toilet Paper Tube

Study the drawing of the cardboard toilet paper tube. Better still, obtain one and study it **carefully**.

Newton wants you to figure out what the cardboard tube looked like **before** it was twisted into a circular shape.

1. Draw what you think it would look like on your own paper.

2. Cut a real toilet paper tube along its lines to check your drawing.

What's the Matter?

Newton Explains Mass and Weight

Just what is matter? This book, your pen, the desk, the air and the Earth are all made of matter. *Matter* is defined as "anything that occupies **space**." A block of wood is matter because it occupies space. When you drive a nail into wood, the nail pushes the wood aside because they are both matter and cannot occupy the same space. The drivers of cars colliding on the freeway soon learn that autos are made of matter and cannot occupy the same space.

The amount of matter in an object is defined as **mass**. The more mass in matter, the harder it is to move it. Mass is measured with a balance and is usually given in metric units of grams or kilograms.

If you are alert, you should be wondering how **weight** differs from mass. The words *weight* and *mass* are practically the same and interchangeable in common usage. But for the precise needs of physicists, they are vastly different.

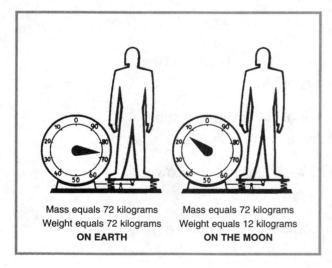

Mass equals 72 kilograms
Weight equals 72 kilograms
ON EARTH

Mass equals 72 kilograms
Weight equals 12 kilograms
ON THE MOON

Mass is defined as "the amount of matter and never changes." A 72-kilogram astronaut has a mass of 72 kilograms on Earth, in space and on the moon. However, he may weigh 72 kilograms on Earth, 0 kilograms in space and only 12 kilograms on the moon. This is because weight is defined as "the pull of gravity on an object." Weight is a measure of the force of gravitational attraction and is measured with a spring scale or balance. The weight of an object depends on both the amount of mass (which never changes) and the pulling force of gravity (which may change from place to place). On the moon, our 72-kilogram astronaut weighs only 12 kilograms because the gravitational pull of the moon is only one sixth of the Earth's gravitational pull.

Name _____

A Quick Review of Matter

Reread page 8. It will help you understand and complete the review sentences. You can use the key words on the right for help.

KEY WORDS
GRAMS
KILOGRAMS
CHANGES
MASS
MATTER
GRAVITY
SPACE
SCALE

1. Matter has _____ and occupies space.

2. Two objects cannot occupy the same _____ at the same time.

3. Mass is a measure of the amount of _____ in an object.

4. Mass is measured on a balance in metric units of _____ and _____.

5. Weight depends on both the mass of an object and the pull of _____.

6. Weight is measured with a spring _____ or a balance.

7. Mass never _____, but weight can vary with an object's location.

How Dense Are You?

Density is an important characteristic of matter. A physicist may need to determine the density of a metal. A geologist must determine the density of rocks. Astronomers will need to calculate the density of planets, moons and stars.

All these scientists use the same definition of *density*. The formula is as follows:

$$\text{Density} = \frac{\text{Weight}}{\text{Volume}}$$

Note: Since we are measuring on Earth we will consider mass and weight to be practically the same.

Name _____

You can find the density of any object by dividing its **weight** by its **volume**. Suppose you wanted to find the density of a rock. Weigh it using a balance or spring scale. Find the rock's volume using a graduate.

Example: A rock weighs 80 grams.
Its volume is 16 milliliters.

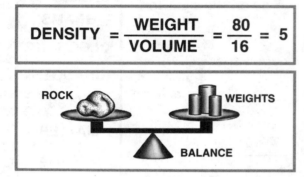

$$\text{DENSITY} = \frac{\text{WEIGHT}}{\text{VOLUME}} = \frac{80}{16} = 5$$

ROCK   WEIGHTS
BALANCE

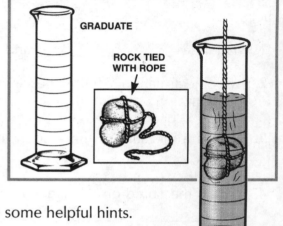

GRADUATE

ROCK TIED WITH ROPE

Newton wants you to measure the density of some convenient objects. Here are some helpful hints.

1. Round off the weight to the nearest gram.

2. Dry the objects off before weighing them.

3. Use the largest sample of each object that can fit inside your graduate.

4. Obtain volume by filling the graduate to a convenient level, submerging the objects and recording the *difference* in volume.

5. Tie a string to the object to lower it **safely**.

6. Use rocks, metal, wood, candles, plastic or anything convenient.

7. Fill out the Density Data Table below.

DENSITY DATA TABLE			
Material Tested	Weight in grams to nearest gram	Volume in milliliters to nearest milliliter	Density = Mass ÷ Volume Round off to one decimal place
1			
2			
3			
4			
5			
6			

10

Name _____

Comparing Density

Water in the metric system was selected to have a **density** of one. This means that one cubic centimeter (also one milliliter) of water weighs exactly one gram.

Any substance having a density less than one will float on water. Any substance having a density **greater** than one will sink.

DENSITY TABLE		
(All density numbers compared to water's density of one.)		
SOLIDS	**METALS**	**LIQUIDS**
BONE 2	ALUMINUM . . .2.7	PURE WATER . . .1
BRICK 1.8	COPPER 8.9	SEA WATER . .1.03
CORK 0.2	GOLD 19.3	ALCOHOL 0.8
ICE 0.92	IRON 7.8	GLYCERINE . . .1.3
MARBLE 2.7	LEAD 11.3	MILK 1.03
PARAFFIN 0.9	SILVER 10.5	TURPENTINE . .0.9
RUBBER 1.2		MERCURY 13.6
BAMBOO 0.3		GASOLINE 0.7
OAK WOOD . .0.7		
PINE WOOD . .0.6		

1. Study the Density Table.

   a. Name five substances that will float on water. _____,

   _____, _____, _____, _____

   b. Name five substances that will sink in water. _____,

   _____, _____, _____, _____

   c. What is the least dense substance on the table?

   d. What is the most dense substance on the table?

   e. Mercury is a liquid with a density of 13.6. Which metal on the table would sink rather than float in mercury? _____

   f. Gasoline has a density of 0.7. Would you expect it to sink or float on water?

   _____

   g. You find a lump of what looks like gold. Based on what you learned in this investigation, how can you find out if it's really gold?

Look up **Archimedes** in a reference book. He had the same gold problem over 2000 years ago. Find out how he solved his "gold crown" problem.

_____

_____

_____

The Characteristics of Matter

Newton Describes Matter

Every kind of matter has characteristics that make it different than any other matter. Lead is very **dense** because it has a lot of molecules packed into a small space. Wood is not as dense.

Glass is **brittle** and shatters easily. Rubber is **flexible** and stretches. Copper wires are **conductors** of both heat and electricity.

Describe the characteristics of a bar of soap. _____

_____

Describe the characteristics of a football. _____

_____

The Big Words of Matter

Here is a chart of some of the physical characteristics of matter. Study it and answer the questions on page 13.

PHYSICAL CHARACTERISTICS OF MATTER		
Property of Matter	**Description of Property**	**Examples**
Texture	How it feels to the touch.	sandpaper, cotton
Luster	How it reflects light.	moon, ball bearing
Brittleness	How easily it shatters.	glass
Malleability	Ability to be pounded into a thin sheet.	gold
Ductility	Ability to be drawn into a thin wire.	copper
Conductivity	Can it let heat or electricity pass through?	copper
Combustibility	Can it burn?	wood
Solubility	Can it dissolve in water?	sugar, salt
Transparent	Can light pass through it almost completely?	clear air
Translucent	Light goes through but you can't see through it clearly.	bathroom window
Opaque	No light can pass through.	metal pan

Name _____

Use the chart on page 12 to answer the following questions:

1. Name three kinds of matter that have a rough texture. _____

_____

2. Name three kinds of matter that have a shiny luster. _____

_____

3. Would ice or wood be more brittle? _____

4. Name three kinds of matter that conduct heat poorly. _____

_____

5. Name three kinds of matter that are not very soluble. _____

_____

6. Would your skin be transparent, translucent or opaque? _____

7. Name something, besides copper, that is both ductile *and* malleable. **Hint:**

Think metals. _____

_____

8. Name three kinds of matter that are combustible. _____

_____

Newton's Viscosity Race

Viscosity is an interesting characteristic of fluid matter. Viscosity is the characteristic of fluids that causes them to resist flowing. Molasses has a high viscosity and resists flowing. Water has a low viscosity and flows easily. Motor oil for engines can have different amounts of viscosity.

Newton wants you to compare the viscosity of various fluids.

1. Obtain a 2' (.61 m) board and cover one side with wax paper or clear plastic wrap.

Name _____

2. Mount it on a table so there is a 30° angle as shown. You could use books at one end.

3. Collect water, rubbing alcohol, syrup, cooking oil, motor oil and any thick fluid of your choice.

4. Place a drop of water at the top of your ramp. Measure how far it slides down your ramp in **10** seconds.

5. Record your answers in the Viscosity Data Table.

6. Repeat for the other fluids. Your choice could be soy sauce, liquid soap, vinegar, etc.

On the basis of your results, list the six fluids in order from the **most** to the **least** viscosity.

1. _____ 2. _____

3. _____ 4. _____

5. _____ 6. _____

VISCOSITY DATA TABLE	
FLUID USED	**DISTANCE IN CENTIMETERS IN 10 SECONDS**
1. water	
2. alcohol	
3. syrup	
4. oil, cooking	
5. oil, motor	
6. your choice	

Newton Wants You to Research Matter

This unit has been about the many interesting characteristics of matter. Newton challenges you to pick one for further research and experimentation.

Pick one characteristic of matter to investigate. Prepare both a written report and a demonstration about your chosen characteristic. The list below has matter characteristics not mentioned in this unit.

adhesion   volatility   salinity   sublimation

cohesion   diffusion   fluorescence   saturation

Good luck!

Superball Olympics

Newton Wants You to Know

All objects in your surroundings differ in their physical characteristics. This activity deals with the properties of **resiliency** and **elasticity**. A compressed object uses these properties to return to its original form.

Imagine a rubber ball and yourself being tossed out of a 10-story window. Both you and the ball would be deformed on impact with the sidewalk. Only the ball is elastic and resilient enough to resist being deformed, bounce back and restore its former shape. Let's test a few objects to check their **resilasticity**.

How High Will I Bounce?

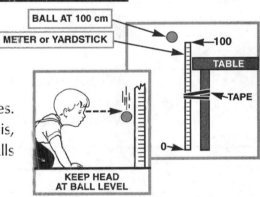

BALL AT 100 cm
METER or YARDSTICK
100
TABLE
TAPE
0
KEEP HEAD
AT BALL LEVEL

You can measure a ball's resilasticity by how high it bounces. Obtain a variety of balls. These can include rubber, beach, tennis, Ping-Pong™, etc. The best bounce will be with very elastic balls called Superballs™.

1. Tape a meterstick to a table as shown. You could also use a yardstick.

2. Drop each ball from the 100-centimeter mark. The **bottom** of the ball should line up with the 100 mark.

3. Measure the bounce to the **nearest centimeter**. Adjust your eye level to measure the **top** of the ball's bounce.

4. To improve accuracy, drop each ball three times to find the average bounce.

5. Record your data on the Ball Bounce Data Table.

BALL BOUNCE DATA TABLE				
TYPE OF BALL	**BOUNCE IN CENTIMETERS**			
	1	**2**	**3**	**AVERAGE**

Name _____

Bounce Off Me

How high a ball bounces depends on the surface it falls upon. Use your **best** bouncing ball to test various surfaces.

Move your meterstick to various areas. Bounce your **best** ball off tile, rugs, plastic, concrete, bricks, cardboard or whatever is available to you. Use the same technique as in "How High Will I Bounce?" Fill out the Surface Bounce Data Table.

SURFACE BOUNCE DATA TABLE				
TYPE OF SURFACE	BOUNCE IN CENTIMETERS			
	1	2	3	AVERAGE

What surface gave you the best bounce? _____

What surface had the least bounce? _____

Newton's Double Bounce

Newton wants to share his favorite trick with you. Obtain large and small balls. Drop any combination of two balls. Be sure the **bottom** ball is at least twice the diameter of the top ball.

Caution! The smaller ball's bounce may astound you. Stay out of its way.

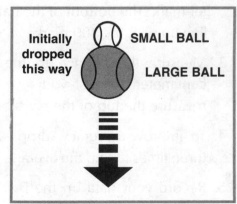

Initially dropped this way — SMALL BALL — LARGE BALL

Egg Matter: A Packaging Contest

Newton Drops His Egg

Newton is human. He makes mistakes. He drops things. Last week he dropped and broke a dozen eggs.

As Newton cleaned up the mess in his kitchen, he thought of how fragile eggs are. He wondered why eggshells were made of such brittle matter. He also wondered what materials would be best for packaging eggs.

Newton loves to research. He found out that in 1996 our farmers produced 62 trillion eggs. On the way to the market, 930 billion broke due to thin, fragile shells or improper handling. This amounts to 1.5% breakage or an incredible $25 million a year loss

Rules for the Egg Package Contest

1. Form teams for this contest.

2. A single **raw** egg will be dropped from the highest safe point in your school.

3. The egg must be packaged within a standard one-pound (.45 kg) coffee can.

4. Nothing must be on the outside of the coffee can. For some designs a few exceptions will be made.

5. Your team may do anything you wish inside the coffee can.

6. At least two different kinds of packaging material must be used. You may use more than two kinds of materials if you wish.

7. Only one package per team.

8. The egg package and detailed drawings of your design are both due on _____.

9. How the contest will be graded.

- Unique and creative use of materials–up to 10 points.

- Colorful, detailed, large drawing showing the cross section of your egg package–up to 10 points.

- Successful drop–egg is not smashed or is only barely cracked–10 points

- Bonus points. Not required. This may actually make your team lose points. Daring, confident teams may try to package two eggs in one coffee can. If neither breaks, you get 10 more points; if only one breaks, you still get five bonus points. If both break, your get zero points.

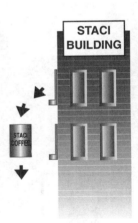

STACI BUILDING

STACI COFFEE

Name _____

Spring Lab: Experimenting with Elastic Matter

Spring Science

Springs have the characteristic of matter called **elasticity**. When stretched within their limits, springs return to their original shape.

Most springs are made of steel or bronze metal. They are first bent into the desired shape. Then they are treated with heat and cold until they maintain that shape.

Springs are everywhere in your life. They click your pens. They cushion your bed. They close doors and operate toys. Spring scales are used to weigh things.

Can you name eight devices that work by springs?

1. _____ 2. _____

3. _____ 4. _____

5. _____ 6. _____

7. _____ 8. _____

Newton Explains Hooke's Law

Robert Hooke (1635-1703) lived in England in the same time period as Newton. He was a great physicist who discovered the law of springs. It is actually called Hooke's Law.

Hooke's Law states that the stretch in a spring is proportional to the weights attached. This means that if a spring stretches 10 centimeters with a five-gram weight, it will stretch 20 centimeters with a 10-gram weight. Hooke's Law assumes that you don't stretch the spring beyond its usual limits.

Spring Scale

Spring Lab: Experimenting with Elastic Matter

Name _____

You are going to prove Hooke's Law for yourself.

1. Obtain a soft spring, a large paper or plastic cup, some string, small marbles of the same size and a ruler.

Note: Springs can be obtained from any hardware store, or you can cut off about 10 turns of a Slinky™ toy. If you have a tight spring, you may have to use heavier objects than marbles for weights.

2. Set up your experiment as shown at the right.

3. Line up your metric ruler so that the "0" centimeters is at the **bottom end** of the spring as shown.

4. Add a marble to the cup and record the new centimeter reading in the Spring Data Table.

5. Keep adding one marble at a time and record the new centimeters.

6. Repeat until you have recorded 10 marbles.

7. Study your data table and review the definition of Hooke's Law.

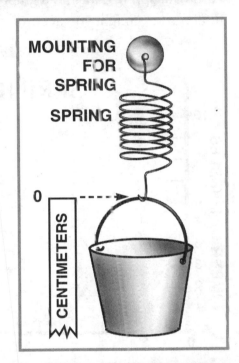

MOUNTING FOR SPRING

SPRING

0

CENTIMETERS

SPRING DATA TABLE										
NUMBER OF MARBLES	1	2	3	4	5	6	7	8	9	10
SPRING STRETCH IN CENTIMETERS										

Explain how your data either proves or disproves Hooke's Law.

_____

_____

_____

_____

Name _____

Graphing Your Spring Data

Newton always turns his experimental data into a graph. A graph helps you to clearly see your results. A graph helps predict what might happen in future experiments.

Turn your spring data into a graph using the form below. Your data should graph out to almost a straight line according to Hooke's Law.

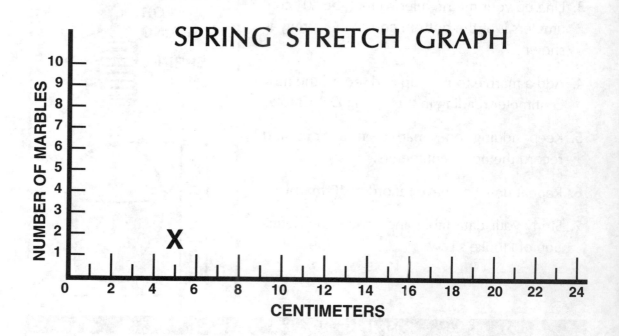

1. Place an *X* for all your data points. For example, if two marbles lengthened the spring to five centimeters, place an *X* as shown.

2. Ignore the sample *X* and place an *X* for each of your data points.

3. Draw the straightest line you can between the *X* points. Use your graph to try to answer the following questions.

How far would your spring have stretched if you had used 12 marbles? _____

_____

How far would your spring have stretched if you had used four and a half marbles?

_____

Name _____

Brainstorming with Springs

Many large companies often call their most creative employees together to dream up new uses for the product they make. This process is called brainstorming. Form teams and combine your massive brain power to brainstorm five novel uses for springs. You should list and sketch the five ideas below and be prepared to demonstrate models of two of your ideas in class.

Your team must have at least two models of your great ideas to present to the class. You could show a set of bookends using springs. Springs can be obtained from hardware stores or borrowed from devices like ballpoint pens.

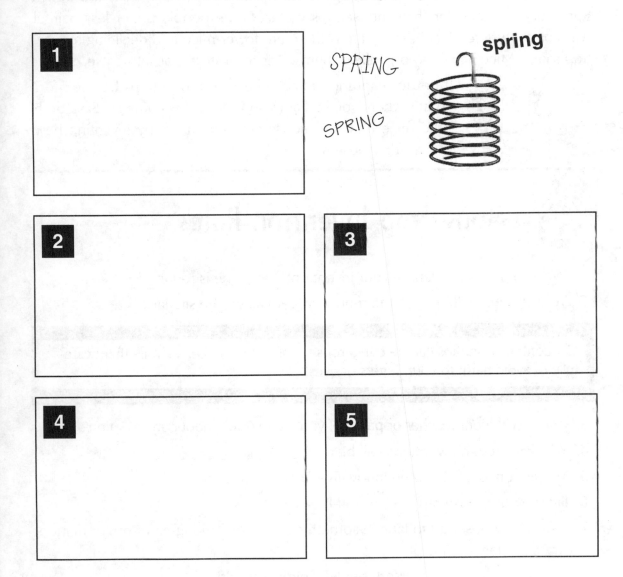

NEWTON'S ACTION LAB
Physical Science 7

Mousetrap Science

Mousetrap Science

Mousetraps use a spring as power to trap mice. A bit of cheese or peanut butter acts as bait to lure careless mice. The spring stores the energy that releases and traps the poor rodent.

The companies that make mousetraps have a problem because sales are down. Some people consider their mousetraps cruel. Some people prefer less painful ways of capturing mice. In some areas there are fewer mice and declining mouse-trap sales. Mice have also organized themselves to protest mousetrap use.

If not for capturing mice, what can mousetraps be used for? That's where you brilliant young scientists come in. Save both the mice and the mousetrap companies by inventing new uses for mousetraps.

Mousetrap Invention Rules

1. Work in teams to prepare your invention. Only one is required.
2. Your teacher will provide the mousetraps so all will be similar.

Caution! Mousetraps can be **dangerous** to more than mice. Handle them **carefully** to avoid harm to your fingers or eyes.

3. Check with your **teacher** or **parent** if you are in doubt about an invention's safety.
4. Your mousetrap inventions will be due _____.
5. You are encouraged to be innovative and creative.
6. Finish your mousetrap device so it looks attractive.
7. Use your mousetrap to launch something, turn something on or off, or demonstrate a science principle.

Work safely! Enjoy yourself!

Name _____

Friction: Friend or Foe?

How Friction Affects Your Life

Every time you move something you must fight three characteristics of matter. **Gravity** resists your efforts. **Inertia** (an object's resistance to change) also fights you. A third characteristic of matter that fights motion is **friction**. Friction is due to two surfaces rubbing.

FORD FRICTION SPECIAL

When you slide a box across the floor, the two surfaces rub and create a frictional force that make your work harder. If both the box and the floor were highly waxed, there would be less surface rubbing. You would be doing less work in moving the box. If you mounted the box on wheels, there would be even less surface contact and you might even enjoy pulling the box.

Friction can be both friend and foe. Forget to put oil in your auto engine and friction destroys it. Without friction between the tires and the road, you couldn't stop a car. Without friction you couldn't play a violin or erase the many mistakes you make in science labs.

Fill out the list below to show you understand friction as a friend or foe.

HELPS PEOPLE	HINDERS PEOPLE
Example – auto brakes	*Example – wears out shoes*
1. _____	1. _____
2. _____	2. _____
3. _____	3. _____
4. _____	4. _____
5. _____	5. _____

Have some friction fun. Place petroleum jelly on a doorknob and try to open the door. Tighten the lid on a jar, soap your hands and try to take the lid off If you try these ideas, you'll learn that friction can be a friend.

Name _____

Friction Produces Heat

When two surfaces rub, they produce heat. The brake shoes that stop your car rub against the wheel and produce heat.

Have you ever rubbed your hands together on a cold day? You are partially warming yourself by the heat of friction.

Try to measure the heat generated by rubbing your hands.

1. Obtain a thermometer.

2. Hold the mercury bulb end of the thermometer firmly in your clenched fist for one full minute.

3. Read the thermometer *while it is still in your hands*. Record the temperature. _____ degrees

4. Rub your hands **vigorously** for one full minute.

5. Quickly place the thermometer in your clenched fist for one minute.

6. Read the temperature as before. Record the temperature after the friction of rubbing. _____ degrees

How much higher was the rubbing temperature than the normal temperature?

_____

What generated the heat that raised the temperature? _____

_____

Developing Your Own Friction Law

Newton won fame for the law of gravity, Archimedes for the law of buoyancy and Einstein for the law relating matter and energy. How would you like to give your name to a new law of friction? All you have to do is to collect data on how pulling force on a sled increases with the addition of extra weights. As a potential genius, you should have no trouble finding an important law somewhere in your data.

Friction: Friend or Foe?

Name _____

1. Obtain a piece of wood about 10 x 40 centimeters to act as a sled.

2. Hammer a nail in one end. Don't hammer it all the way. The nail should stick above the board.

3. Obtain a spring scale and five **unopened** soda cans.

4. You can do the following activities on a long table or on the floor.

5. Place one full soda can on the sled.

6. Attach the spring scale to the protruding nail.

7. Practice pulling the sled. The pull should not be upwards but parallel to the table or floor.

8. Observe and read the weight in grams on the spring scale while **moving the sled with a steady pull**.

9. Record the steady pull in the Friction Data Table next to *1 can*.

10. Repeat using two, three, four and five cans at a time.

FRICTION DATA TABLE	
Number of Full Soda Can	**Spring Scale Reading for Steady Pull-Grams**
1 can	
2 cans	
3 cans	
4 cans	
5 cans	

Time for your **friction law**. Study your Friction Data Table and write a short statement about weights (soda cans) and the grams of pull needed to move them. Make Newton and Einstein proud of you.

_____

_____

_____

_____

Name _____

Rolling Friction

Sliding friction as done with our wooden sled was fine for prehistoric man dragging around his few possessions. Our modern vehicles work much easier using ball bearings for **rolling friction** instead of sliding friction. Ball bearings can help move objects weighing tons with very little effort.

Back to the soda cans. Why not use them as a poor substitute for ball bearings and try to measure how little force it takes to roll a heavy table?

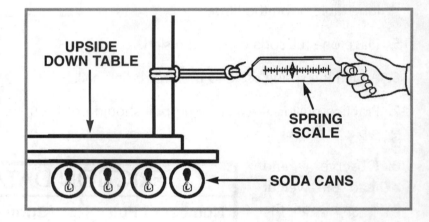

1. Get help to turn a small table upside down.

2. Tie a string to one leg and attach your spring scale to the string.

3. Try to pull the table along the floor.

   Describe what happened? _____

   _____

4. Now **carefully** place four or five soda cans under the table as shown.

5. Try to pull the rolling table with your spring scale.

6. Measure the grams of pull needed to keep the table in **steady** motion. _____ grams

Why is it easier to roll a heavy object on wheels rather than sliding it along?

_____

Besides using wheels and ball bearings, how else could you reduce friction between

two rubbing surfaces? _____

_____

Spoolmobile Contest: Overcoming Friction

Newton Wants You to Know

Any moving object has friction. Friction is due to two surfaces rubbing together. Their rubbing generates heat which wastes energy.

You are going to build a **spoolmobile**. This is a simple device that uses a rubber band to store energy. Stored energy is called **potential energy** When your spoolmobile is released, the stored energy is converted to moving energy. Scientists call moving energy **kinetic** energy.

In this lab you are asked to apply your scientific genius to building a better **spoolmobile**. If you are successful, future generations of Americans will desert their Fords and Chevrolets to ride the freeways on your Spoolmobile.

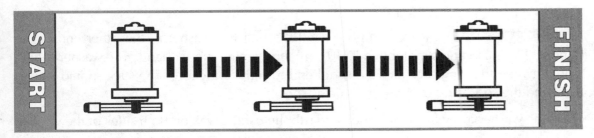

Spoolmobile Physics

Designing a winning spoolmobile is an engineering challenge. Knowing the following physics principles will help you build a better spoolmobile:

Friction. When the moving parts of the spoolmobile rub, they produce heat. This causes a loss of energy that could be used for forward motion. You can cut down friction by using a lubricant such as candle wax, oil or graphite. Try cutting down friction by using washers or by sanding or steel-wooling parts in contact.

Stability. Spoolmobiles have a tendency to spin off the track. You can increase stability by varying the size and length of the stick or using a stick or both sides. Adding some weight to the spool or using a nail or other metal can help.

Name _____

Traction. Your spoolmobile will tend to lose contact with the ground and spin so that it goes nowhere. This is the same as if your mom or dad drove around on smooth bald tires. You can improve traction by roughing up the spool rims. Adding weights to the spool or stick will help traction as well as stability. Unfortunately, the added weight can increase friction and use up your stored energy.

Building Your Spoolmobile

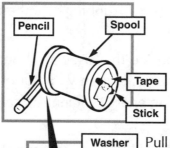

Obtain a standard or large size sewing thread spool. Many different kinds can be used. Find some thin sticks (an unsharpened pencil will do), **thick** rubber bands, a shiny washer and a candle. You will be using the candle wax as a lubricant to cut friction. The thick rubber band should be slightly longer than the spool. Study the diagram on the left. It shows how to construct a spoolmobile.

Pull the rubber band or bands through the spool hole. Place a very short stick through the rubber band so the band cannot pull back into the spool. Tape the small stick to the end of the spool so it doesn't move. Neither the stick nor the tape should extend beyond the spool's end.

Place a rubber band through the washer at the other end of the spool. Place a longer stick (about 4" [10 cm]) through the rubber band. The washer should be between the long stick and the spool end to reduce friction. The stick should extend beyond the spool end only on one side as shown.

Pull the washer away from the spool, and rub the candle wax on both sides of the washer.

Wind up your rubber band as much as can be done **safely**. Place your spoolmobile on the floor and watch with pride as it converts stored potential into moving kinetic energy.

Newton Wants You to Build a Better Spoolmobile

The **spoolmobile** you built is like Henry Ford's first automobile. It works, but it has problems. It doesn't go far. It doesn't always go straight. It is unstable. The parts move against each other to create friction.

Restudy page 27 and this page on Spoolmobile Physics. Try to improve yours, or scrap it and build a better one. Try changing spool sizes, using better or more rubber bands or different size sticks. Try other lubricants besides candle wax to cut friction.

Newton challenges you!

28

Periodic Table Lab

Newton Introduces the Periodic Table

All living and nonliving matter is made of **atoms**. There are only 92 natural atoms found in the world. These 92 atoms combine to form the **molecules** that make up all matter around us.

The water molecule shown on the right is made of two hydrogen atoms combined with one oxygen atom. Common table salt combines one sodium atom with one chlorine atom.

This lab is designed as an intellectual challenge. The only materials required are your great mind and the Periodic Table provided. You may also use any reference sources available.

If you have trouble with this lab, you can blame it on the Russian scientist Dmitri Ivanovitch Mendeleev. Mendeleev invented the Periodic Table. He, in turn, can blame it on the frustrations of being the youngest of 17 children in his family. Good luck and do the best you can. It might help to work in pairs.

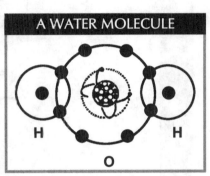

A WATER MOLECULE

H   H
O

Newton Explains the Periodic Table

See the Periodic Table on page 30.

1. Atoms 1 to 92 are atoms found in nature.

2. Atoms 93 to 103 are created by scientists.

3. Atoms listed below each other have something in common.

4. Atom *symbols always* start with a capital letter followed, if needed, by small letters.

3	——— Atomic number
Lithium	——— Name
Li	——— Symbol
6.939	——— Atomic mass (weight)
2,1	——— Electron arrangement

5. Atoms are numbered from 1 to 103. This is usually in order of the number of electrons.

6. Atom weights (mass) are not in grams but in relative weight compared to hydrogen as a weight of one.

7. Electron arrangement tells you the number of electron shells and the amount of electrons in each shell. Lithium has two shells. There are two electrons in the first shell and only one electron in the second shell.

Name _____

PERIODIC TABLE

Key (example):

3
Lithium — Name
Li — Symbol
6.939 — Atomic mass (weight)
2,1 — Electron arrangement

3 — Atomic number

Groups

Group IA
| 1 Hydrogen **H** 1.00797 1 |
| 3 Lithium **Li** 6.939 2,1 |
| 11 Sodium **Na** 22.9898 2,8,1 |
| 19 Potassium **K** 39.102 2,8,8,1 |
| 37 Rubidium **Rb** 85.4678 2,8,18,8,1 |
| 55 Cesium **Cs** 132.905 -18,18,8,1 |
| 87 Francium **Fr** (223) -18,32,18,8,1 |

Group IIA
| 4 Beryllium **Be** 9.01218 2,2 |
| 12 Magnesium **Mg** 24.312 2,8,2 |
| 20 Calcium **Ca** 40.08 2,8,8,2 |
| 38 Strontium **Sr** 87.62 2,8,18,8,2 |
| 56 Barium **Ba** 137.34 -18,18,8,2 |
| 88 Radium **Ra** (227) -18,32,18,8,2 |

Groups

21 Scandium **Sc** 44.9559 2,8,9,2	22 Titanium **Ti** 47.90 2,8,10,2	23 Vanadium **V** 50.942 2,8,11,2	24 Chromium **Cr** 51.9380 2,8,13,1	25 Manganese **Mn** 54.9380 2,8,13,2	26 Iron **Fe** 55.847 -2,8,14,2	27 Cobalt **Co** 58.9332 2,8,15,2	28 Nickel **Ni** 58.71 -2,8,16,2	29 Copper **Cu** 63.54 2,8,18,1	30 Zinc **Zn** 65.47 2,8,18,2
39 Yttrium **Y** 88.905 2,8,18,9,2	40 Zirconium **Zr** 91.22 2,8,18,10,2	41 Niobium **Nb** 92.906 2,8,18,12,1	42 Molybdenum **Mo** 95.94 2,8,18,13,1	43 Technetium **Tc** (99) 2,8,18,14,1	44 Ruthenium **Ru** 101.07 2,8,18,15,1	45 Rhodium **Rh** 102.905 2,8,18,16,1	46 Palladium **Pd** 106.4 2,8,18,18	47 Silver **Ag** 107.870 2,8,18,18,1	48 Cadmium **Cd** 112.40 2,8,18,18,2
57 to 71*	72 Hafnium **Hf** 178.49 -18,32,10,2	73 Tantalum **Ta** 180.947 -18,32,11,2	74 Tungsten **W** 183.85 -18,32,12,2	75 Rhenium **Re** 186.2 -18,32,13,2	76 Osmium **Os** 190.2 -18,32,14,2	77 Iridium **Ir** 192.2 -18,32,15,2	78 Platinum **Pt** 195.09 -18,32,17,1	79 Gold **Au** 196.967 -18,32,18,1	80 Mercury **Hg** 200.59 -18,32,18,2
89 to 103**	104 (257) (259)	105 (260) (261)	106 (259)	107 (262)	108 (266)	109 (266)			

Groups IIIA–VIIIA

IIIA	IVA	VA	VIA	VIIA	VIIIA
					2 Helium **He** 4.0026 2
5 Boron **B** 10.81 2,3	6 Carbon **C** 12.011 2,4	7 Nitrogen **N** 14.0067 2,5	8 Oxygen **O** 15.9994 2,6	9 Fluorine **F** 18.9984 2,7	10 Neon **Ne** 20.183 2,8
13 Aluminum **Al** 26.9815 2,8,3	14 Silicon **Si** 28.086 2,8,4	15 Phosphorus **P** 30.9738 2,8,5	16 Sulfur **S** 32.064 2,8,6	17 Chlorine **Cl** 35.453 2,8,7	18 Argon **Ar** 39.948 2,8,8
31 Gallium **Ga** 69.72 2,8,18,3	32 Germanium **Ge** 72.59 2,8,18,4	33 Arsenic **As** 72.9216 2,8,18,5	34 Selenium **Se** 78.96 2,8,18,6	35 Bromine **Br** 79.909 2,8,18,7	36 Krypton **Kr** 83.80 2,8,18,8
49 Indium **In** 114.82 2,8,18,18,3	50 Tin **Sn** 118.69 2,8,18,18,4	51 Antimony **Sb** 121.75 2,8,18,18,5	52 Tellurium **Te** 127.60 2,8,18,18,6	53 Iodine **I** 126.9044 2,8,18,18,7	54 Xenon **Xe** 131.30 2,8,18,18,8
81 Thallium **Tl** 204.37 -18,32,18,3	82 Lead **Pb** 207.19 -18,32,18,4	83 Bismuth **Bi** 208.980 -18,32,18,5	84 Polonium **Po** (210) -18,32,18,6	85 Astatine **At** (210) -18,32,18,7	86 Radon **R** (222) -18,32,18,8

* Lanthanides (57 to 71)

| 57 Lanthanum **La** 138.91 -18,9,2 | 58 Cerium **Ce** 140.12 -18,20,8,2 | 59 Praseodymium **Pr** 140.907 -18,21,8,2 | 60 Neodymium **Nd** 144.24 -18,22,8,2 | 61 Promethium **Pm** (145) -18,23,8,2 | 62 Samarium **Sm** 150.4 -18,24,8,2 | 63 Europium **Eu** 151.96 -18,25,8,2 | 64 Gadolinium **Gd** 157.25 -18,25,9,2 | 65 Terbium **Tb** 158.924 -18,27,8,2 | 66 Dysprosium **Dy** 162.50 -18,28,8,2 | 67 Holmium **Ho** 164.930 -18,29,8,2 | 68 Erbium **Er** 167.26 -18,30,8,2 | 69 Thulium **Tm** 168.934 -18,31,8,2 | 70 Ytterbium **Yb** 173.04 -18,32,8,2 | 71 Lutetium **Lu** 174.97 -18,32,9,2 |

** Actinides (89 to 103)

| 89 Actinium **Ac** (227) -18,32,18,9,2 | 90 Thorium **Th** 232.038 -18,32,18,10,2 | 91 Protactinium **Pa** (231) -18,32,20,9,2 | 92 Uranium **U** 238.03 -18,32,21,9,2 | 93 Neptunium **Np** (237) -18,32,22,9,2 | 94 Plutonium **Pu** (242) -18,32,24,8,2 | 95 Americium **Am** (243) -18,32,25,8,2 | 96 Curium **Cm** (245) -18,32,25,9,2 | 97 Berkelium **Bk** (249) -18,32,26,9,2 | 98 Californium **Cf** (250) -18,32,28,8,2 | 99 Einsteinium **Es** (254) -18,32,29,8,2 | 100 Fermium **Fm** (252) -18,32,30,8,2 | 101 Mendelevium **Md** (256) -18,32,31,8,2 | 102 Nobelium **No** (254) -18,32,32,8,2 | 103 Lawrencium **Lw** (257) -18,32,32,9,2 |

30

Name _____

Newton Wants You to Have Fun with the Periodic Table

Atomic Animals

List the atoms, as done in the example below, whose symbols spell out these animals. In some cases, you may have to stretch your imagination to have them come out right.

> **Example:** Lion = Li O N = Lithium + Oxygen + Nitrogen

Seal =   Snakes =

Bear =   Shark =

Cow =   Rhinoceros =

1. Make up three atomic animals on your own. _____

_____

2. Try to find atoms that spell out your last name. It doesn't have to be exact.

_____

_____

Atomic Bonus

Man's latest count shows well over 100 atoms. This is a long way from the approximately 63 which Mendeleev knew. Let's pretend that scientists have suddenly discovered number 120 and can produce tons of it. Could you dream up some characteristics of this new atom which would make it very valuable to mankind?

_____

_____

_____

_____

Name _____

Periodic Table Practice

Fill in the missing spaces in the atom worksheet below.

	ATOMIC NUMBER	ATOMIC SYMBOL	ATOM NAME	ATOMIC WT. (round off to whole number)	USE AND OTHER INFORMATION FROM YOUR EXPERIENCE OR A REFERENCE SOURCE
1	2	He	Helium	4	balloons – dirigibles
2	20				
3		B			
4			Carbon		
5					used in signs – glows with electricity
6		Cl			
7	11				
8			Silicon		
9			Argon		
10				32	
11	22				
12		Cu			
13		Fe			
14			Silver	108	
15		Sn			used in tin cans
16			Gold		
17	82				
18		Ra			
19		K	Potassium		
20				24	used in lightweight airplane parts
21	94				
22		Hg			used in thermometers and barometers
ADD THREE MORE OF YOUR CHOICE BELOW					
23					
24					
25					

32

Name _____

NEWTON'S
ACTION LAB
Physical
Science
11

Puzzling Atoms

1. The **full** names of 55 different atoms can be found below.

2. There are **no symbols** used.

3. The names of the atoms can appear forward, backward, up, down or diagonal.

4. Circle each atom you find.

5. Use the Periodic Table on page 30 for help.

6. An atom may appear more than once.

HAPPY ATOM
HUNTING!

```
N E G O R T I N S C A N D I U M A A R G M B
E A M B E R Y L L I U M E R E P P O C M O I
O S P O T A S S I U M E R C U R Y C H U L R
N O A R A C H R O R U F L U S T Z I R I Y I
E X S O D I U M A G N E S I U M I N O T B D
O Y E N I M O R S O C H L O R I N E M N D I
O G Y M U N I M U L A I N D I U C L I O E U
A E M U I N A T I T C M U I R O H T U R N M
D N O G R A M P H O S P H O R U S O M T U M
I R O N I U M A N G A F S E S R U L E S M P
N O O R I U U G A L L I U M A E E N O N E X
M B O R I U I M M U I L E H S K L V A N A D
H E T C E N H C O B A L T A C K C E L L O S
A T L E A D T H V A N A D I U M A E N L S C
Y A R S E N I C I O D I N E U A X C S I S E
C R A D O N L M U I D A R I M N M M H I U M
D L O G E R M A N I U M O U O G U U A M U M
A Z I R C O N I U M Y I I T R A I I F U N M
T E C H N E T I U M O N P R O N B R N I U M
H T U M S I B O O V A Y Y N R E O A I M I U
R H E N I U M O R R R R R D I U S I B U S S I
M U N I T A L P U K R Y R T O E N O M O L D
```

33

TLC10144 Copyright © Teaching & Learning Company, Carthage, IL 62321-0010

Name _____

Edible Atoms

Newton Takes You Inside Atoms

Atoms are extremely tiny. You couldn't pick up an atom with the smallest tweezers in the world. You can't even see atoms. Yet scientists have discovered the inside structure of atoms.

You can use the Periodic Table on page 30 to learn the inside structure of atoms. Let's use atom number 3 called **Lithium** as an example. See the drawings to the right.

1. Its atomic number is **3**. Therefore, Lithium has three electrons.

2. Notice the numbers **2,1** on the bottom of the Lithium box. It tells you there are **two electron shells**. Two electrons are in the first shell and only one electron is in the second or outer shell.

3. Notice the atom weight is 6.939. Round this off to 7. This means that the Lithium atom has a total of seven protons and neutrons inside its nucleus.

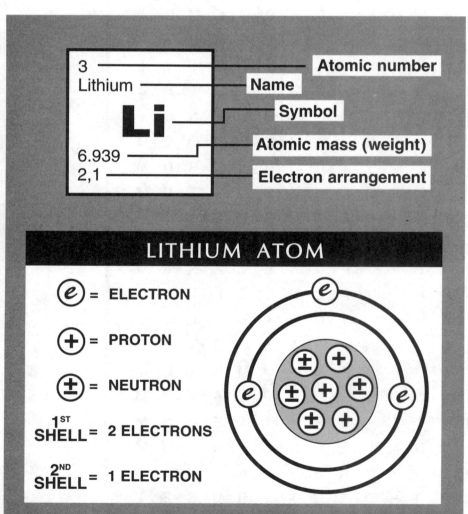

3	**Atomic number**
Lithium	**Name**
Li	**Symbol**
6.939	**Atomic mass (weight)**
2,1	**Electron arrangement**

LITHIUM ATOM

(e) = ELECTRON

(+) = PROTON

(±) = NEUTRON

1ST SHELL = 2 ELECTRONS

2ND SHELL = 1 ELECTRON

Name _____

4. All normal atoms have the same number of protons as electrons. Therefore, your Lithium atom must have 3 protons and 4 neutrons to add up to 7.

5. Protons are given the symbol ⊕. Neutrons are given the symbol ⊕.

---

20 Calcium # Ca 40.08 2,8,8,2	**Another Example:** Find the atom called Calcium. Its number is 20. It has 20 electrons. The shell has 2 electrons in the inner shell, 8 in the next shell, 8 in the next shell and 2 in the outer shell for a total of 20. The atom weight is 40, since the atom number is 20 it has 20 protons ⊕ leaving room for 20 neutrons ⊕.

Newton Hungers for Atoms

Newton wants you to build an **edible atom**. Here are some rules and hints to get you started.

1. All electrons, protons and neutrons must be made of food.

2. The materials holding up your atom do not have to be edible. You can use string, wire, plastic, wood, etc.

3. You may partner up with someone to build a super edible atom.

4. Use cheap food where possible. This contest is not encouraging food or money waste.

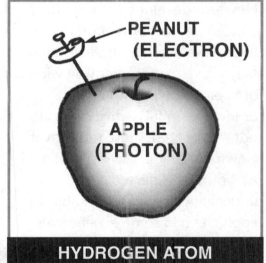

PEANUT (ELECTRON)

APPLE (PROTON)

HYDROGEN ATOM

5. It is not recommended that you eat your completed atom. It may not meet health standards.

6. Concentrate on atoms below number 40 to avoid complications.

7. Attach your name and the atom name to your edible atom.

8. Extra credit for ingenuity, color and humor.

Get to work! Up and atom!

Name _____

Inertia: Newton's First Law of Motion

It's the Law

There are many ways of setting matter in motion. You can drop it and let gravity accelerate it. You can use a rocket engine or a sling-shot. In all cases, matter is moved by a **force** that overcomes the other forces acting on it.

Newton developed three laws concerning matter in motion. All three laws assume an ideal situation where matter is moving without being slowed by air resistance or friction. In this activity, you are not expected to rediscover Newton's famous laws of motion. All you are expected to do is to understand them and be able to apply them in some experiments.

NEWTON'S FIRST LAW OF MOTION

An object at **rest** tends to remain at rest.
An object in **motion** tends to remain in motion in a straight line at a steady speed.

Newton's first law is based upon a property of matter discovered by Galileo called **inertia**. *Inertia* is defined as "matter's resistance to change." Everything that has **mass** has inertia. Mass is roughly equal to weight. The more mass in an object, the more inertia it has and the more it resists change.

Newton's Second Law of Motion

Newton Explains Force, Mass and Acceleration

Newton loves to use big words. His first law introduced us to **inertia**. Now we have to learn three more big words to be able to understand Newton's second law of motion. Study the diagrams on this page that explain **mass**, **force** and **acceleration**.

Now let us put these big words together as Newton's Second Law of Motion.

MASS

The amount of material in an object. Similar to, but not exactly the same as weight.

NEWTON'S SECOND LAW OF MOTION

The acceleration of an object depends upon its mass and the applied force.

Newton's first law tells us that, in an ideal situation, an object placed in motion will keep on moving in a straight line forever.

The second law tells us what happens when a force is applied to such a moving body. Any change in speed, which we have defined as *acceleration*, depends on how much force is applied and how much mass is involved.

The more force we apply, the more the object is accelerated. The more mass (which means more inertia and resistance to change), the less the object is accelerated.

FORCE

A push or pull.

ACCELERATION

Change in the speed of an object.

Name _____

Newton's Acceleration Ramp

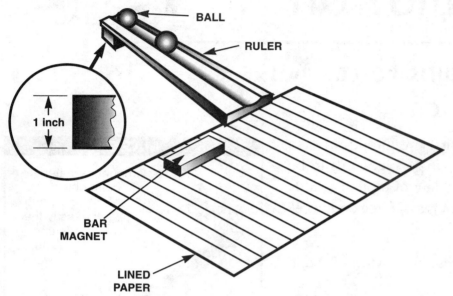

BALL

RULER

1 inch

BAR
MAGNET

LINED
PAPER

1. Obtain a sheet of lined paper, a marble, one large ball bearing, one small ball bearing and a magnet.

   You will also need a ruler with a groove in the center to serve as a ramp. If needed, tape two rulers together with space between to act as a groove.

2. Set up your materials on a tabletop as shown in the diagram.

Your magnet's *position* will vary depending on its strength.

3. Roll your marble down the full ramp past the magnet. Mark the spot where the marble left the lined paper. Describe what happened to the moving marble.

_____

_____

_____

Newton Hint: Marbles are not affected by magnetism.

4. Roll your *small* ball bearing down the full ramp.

You may have to reposition your magnet. Again, mark the spot where the ball bearing left the lined paper. What happened to the ball bearing as it went past the magnetic **force**?

Name _____

Newton Hint: The magnetic force affected the small ball bearing's **direction** and **acceleration**.

---

5. Roll your *large* ball bearing down the full ramp past the magnet. Adjust the magnet if necessary. Again, mark the spot where the large ball bearing left the lined paper.

Compare what happened to the large and small ball bearings as they rolled past the

magnetic force. _____

Newton Challenge: The magnetic **force** remained the same, but you have changed the **mass** and, perhaps, the **acceleration**.

Newton Challenge: Without looking back at Newton's second law, can you state

it below? _____

_____

_____

The Earth Obeys Newton's Laws

You know that the Earth orbits around the sun. This can be explained by Newton's first and second laws.

The Earth is moving in its path around the sun at about 67,000 miles (107,870 km) per hour. If there were no force of gravity, the Earth would spin out of orbit and go in a **straight line** until it passes another gravity force. Here's how to demonstrate this concept.

1. Obtain a 4' (1.2 m) string, a long nail and either a lightweight Styrofoam™ or sponge ball.

2. Tie the string **securely** to the nail as shown.

3. Place the pointed end of the nail halfway into the ball.

4. **Go outside** and whirl the ball around your head gently.

5. Now speed up the rotation until the ball leaves the nail.

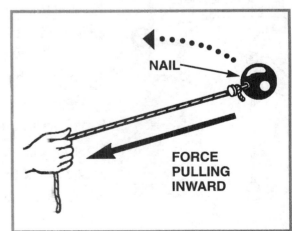

NAIL

FORCE PULLING INWARD

Name _____

Observe the path of the loose ball. Repeat the experiment a few times to get a better look. What was the path of the free ball? _____

_____

Newton Hint: The ball is obeying Newton's first law.

Assume the ball was the Earth circling in orbit. The string imitated the force that kept it circling. What is the real "force" that keeps the Earth from flying into space?

_____

_____

Satellites Also Obey Newton's Law

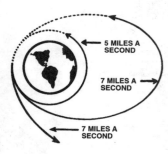

Earth satellites provide us with radio, television and telephone service. Satellites can photograph the Earth, help predict weather and spy on our enemies.

Satellite orbits obey the same Newton laws as the Earth does. Satellites are lifted a certain distance above the Earth and then given a speed of about five miles (8.05 km) per second (18,000 miles [28,980 km] per hour). At that speed the force of gravity just balances the satellite's forward motion and an orbit is maintained.

If the satellite gets lower or is slowed down by space debris, it would take a path back to Earth. If the satellite is sped up to seven miles (11.27 km) per second, it breaks the force of gravity like your ball and roars into space.

Let's make a simple device that mimics how acceleration and force combine to place objects in orbit.

1. Attach a small rubber ball to 3' (.90 m) of string.
2. Run the string through a spool and attach some weights (washers, nuts, etc.) to the opposite end.
3. The weights should be at least twice as heavy as the ball.
4. **Go outside.** Hold the spool firmly, and rotate the ball slowly and then rapidly.
5. What did the weight do?
6. Stop rotating and note how fast the ball spins as it is pulled inward.
7. What did the weight do?

Do some research on planet speed and distance from the sun. You will find a pattern that is explained by Newton's laws.

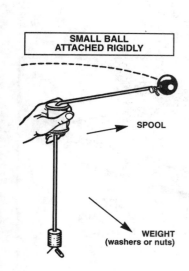

SMALL BALL
ATTACHED RIGIDLY

SPOOL

WEIGHT
(washers or nuts)

42

Action and Reaction: Newton's Third Law of Motion

Newton Explains His Third Law of Motion

Newton's first law of motion dealt with the inertia of matter. Newton's second law tied together the concepts of force, mass and acceleration. His third law is the simplest to understand.

NEWTON'S THIRD LAW OF MOTION

For every action there is an equal and opposite reaction.

Examples of Action and Reaction

Imagine holding on to a garden hose with water spurting out at high speed. You have to hold the hose firmly because, as the water spurts out, the hose wants to move in an opposite direction. That is why it often takes two firefighters to hold a fire hose.

Turn on the water in a garden hose **without** holding onto the nozzle. The hose wiggles like a snake.

You have seen people fire a rifle. As the bullet moves forward, the rifle recoils backward in the opposite direction.

Imagine yourself on a skateboard next to a wall. You push against the wall and send you and your skateboard in the opposite direction. Imagine jumping forward off your skateboard. Your skateboard moves in the opposite direction.

All the above are examples of Newton's third law. In each case there is an action and an equal but opposite reaction.

Name _____

On the left is a model of a steam-driven auto. It was designed, but not built, over 200 years ago. The boiler was heated to produce steam. The steam was ejected toward the rear. The car was supposed to obey Newton's third law and react forward.

Balloon Rockets

Real rockets (and jet engines) work by obeying Newton's third law. Gas flowing out the rear end causes the rocket to move in the opposite direction.

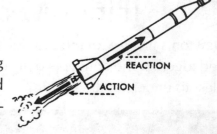

Balloons can substitute for rockets to demonstrate action and reaction.

Simple Balloon Rocket

1. Blow up a balloon to almost maximum size.

2. Tape a 2" (5 cm) section of a large diameter straw inside the neck to act as a rocket nozzle. You may flatten the end of the straw to make a smaller nozzle.

3. Hold your rocket engine high over your head and let go.

Describe what happened in terms of Newton's third law. _____

_____

_____

Better Balloon Rocket

1. Tie a 40' or 45' (12 or 15 m) string about 3' (.90 m) high in a convenient place.

2. Place a straw over the untied end.

Name _____

3. Blow up a balloon, twist the end and attach a paper clip so that the air cannot escape.

4. Tape the full balloon to the straw.

5. Hold the string tight.

6. Release the paper clip and your rocket is off.

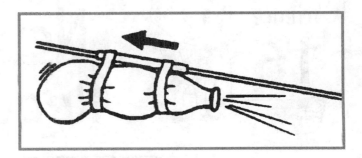

Newton would like you to modify this balloon rocket so that it works better. Are you up to the challenge?

An Action Reaction Water Can

Rotating lawn sprinklers are based upon the law of action and reaction. Here is how to build a rotating sprinkler can.

1. Obtain an empty tin can that held about 16 oz. (45 g).

2. Punch two holes on the open top at opposite sides of the can.

3. Tie a string through the two holes to suspend the can as shown.

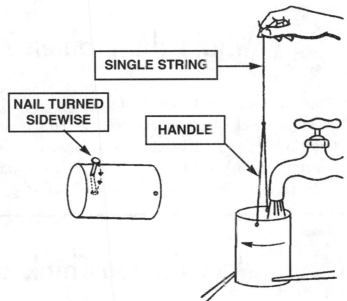

4. Punch a hole near the bottom of the can. Twist the nail sideways so the hole is in a direction parallel to the bottom.

5. Punch a second hole on the opposite side of the can. Again twist it in the same direction as the other bottom hole. This is to insure that both holes emit water in the same direction.

6. The next steps are best done outdoors or over a sink.

7. Hold your can under a faucet (as shown) and observe action and reaction.

8. The device also works without the faucet if just filled with water.

Newton's Action Reaction Puzzler

Which Way Will It Move?

A cork is floating in a large jar of water. It is kept in the center of the jar of water by a string tied to it and attached to the lid. The entire jar is given a **quick, sharp shove** along a tabletop.

What's the Problem?

What will be the **first** motion of the cork when the jar is given the quick, sharp shove? Will the cork remain *centered* in the jar? Will the cork move forward in the *same* direction as the shove? Or will the cork move backward in the jar in a direction opposite of the shove?

What Do You Think Will Happen?

What is your prediction? _____

_____

Can you give a reasonable explanation for your prediction? _____

_____

_____

Newton fools most people with this puzzler. Before you read the answer key, think of what happens when you are in a car that suddenly moves forward. How is the cork in the jar of water different than you in a car?

NEWTON'S
ACTION LAB
Physical
Science
17

Momentum Lab: Transferring the Energy of Motion

Newton Explains Momentum

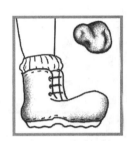

Physicists study matter and energy. An object can have both matter (mass) and energy (velocity or speed). The combination of mass and velocity is called **momentum**.

Momentum = mass times velocity

Momentum is best thought of as a **quantity** of **motion**. A 50-pound (22.5 kg) rock resting on top of your foot may not hurt. The same 50-pound (22.5 kg) rock falling from a height of 10' (3 m) would certainly have enough mass times velocity to damage your foot. A light feather in a 100 mile (161 km) per hour hurricane could have enough momentum (quantity of motion) to penetrate a tree.

Momentum explains how **sound** travels. As you talk, the air molecules near your vocal cords are given the energy to move. They bounce against other air molecules. This transfers the momentum to air molecules near a listener's eardrums.

Momentum also explains how **heat** travels. When you hold a hot iron, the heat molecules in the metal transfer their momentum energy to the molecules in your hand.

Experimenting with Momentum

1. Obtain 10 large marbles or ball bearings of the **same size**.

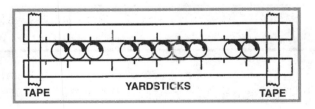

TAPE YARDSTICKS TAPE

Name _____

2. Tape the ends of two yardsticks to a tabletop as shown. The distance between the yardsticks should be wide enough to allow the marbles or ball bearings to roll between them easily.

3. Study the Momentum Data Table below. It tells you how to start each momentum experiment and how to record the results.

4. Study the example in the data table. It shows two marbles being shoved into nine stationary marbles.

5. Set up the marbles as shown in position one. You are slowly shoving one marble into nine stationary marbles. Show your results on the right side of the data table.

6. Repeat for marble positions two through ten.

MOMENTUM DATA TABLE

POSITION OF STARTING MARBLES	POSITION AFTER MOMENTUM TRANSFER
EXAMPLE	
1 SLOW	
2 FAST	
3	
4	
5	
6	
USE YOUR OWN IDEAS BELOW	
7	
8	
9	
10	

48

Name _____

Newton Explains Your Results

Both Newton and Galileo worked on experiments like these. They made discoveries about the laws of momentum and the laws of impact.

The momentum of your marbles was a product of the marbles' mass (weight to you) and velocity (speed to you). Increasing the momentum of the marbles does not change the experiment's results.

When you rolled two marbles into the center pile, as in the example, each impacted **separately** though your eyes could not see it. The second ball struck a microsecond later than the first. Thus, you had two separate impacts pushing through the center marbles and causing the two end marbles to be ejected to the right.

Momentum Freedom

Here's your chance to use your initiative and imagination. Plan a momentum energy transfer experiment of your own. Use marbles, bearings, rubber balls, etc. Change the size of your marbles, bounce them off something, have them move on a curved or tilted ramp, etc. You will be given time to plan your momentum freedom experiment. You must bring in any special equipment you need. You might want to work in teams.

Description of Your Plan

Give sketches and details. Describe it clearly so that even your teacher can understand it. _____

_____

_____

_____

Data Table

Construct a data table to organize the data you collect from your Momentum Freedom. All experiments result in some data.

Name _____

Momentum Challenge: Geo Versus Cadillac

Newton's Puzzler Description

One day Newton was flying as a passenger in a helicopter. Suddenly the pilot frantically screamed that he was having engine trouble. He had to get rid of some weight rapidly or the helicopter would crash. Of course, Newton volunteered to jump out to save the aircraft. Since the helicopter was only a few feet above a freeway, Newton had to jump in front of moving traffic. As he looked down, he saw he only had two choices. He could jump in front of a slow-moving, heavy Cadillac or in front of a fast-moving, light Geo Metro. It had to be one or the other. Newton jumped in front of the _____?_____.

What's the Problem?

Would Newton be hurt more by jumping in front of the heavy Cadillac or the light Geo Metro?

What Do You Think Will Happen?

Which car should Newton jump in front of? Explain the reason for your car choice.

_____

_____

_____

Name _____

How to Test Newton's Puzzler

You could obtain a Cadillac, a Geo Metro and a helicopter and then reenact the puzzler. Or you can solve it in an instant like Newton did just before he jumped. He used a math formula to make a rapid calculation of which car had the least **momentum**.

Momentum is defined by scientists as the "quantity of motion." It is found by multiplying the mass of each car by its velocity. What this means is that what hurts you in a collision with a car is not the mass alone or the velocity alone but the **product** of both. A feather with a mass of ⅓ ounce moving at a velocity of 100 miles (161 km) per hour in a hurricane may have enough momentum to penetrate a tree.

> Momentum is one of Newton's favorite subjects. He thinks that you may need some help in understanding the words used in this puzzler. **Mass** refers to the amount of matter in an object. It differs from **weight** in that weight depends on the pull of gravity and mass does not. The word **velocity** is the rate that an object moves in space in a given direction. Outside of the fact that velocity has a direction, it is similar to what you often call **speed**.

Formula you need to use in this puzzler:

> Momentum = mass x velocity

Here's the data you will need to solve this puzzler:

Cadillac
Mass equals 4500 pounds (2025 kg)
Velocity equals 20 miles (32.2 km) per hour

Geo Metro
Mass equals 1700 pounds (765 kg)
Velocity equals 70 miles (112.7 km) per hour

1. Multiply the mass times the velocity for the Cadillac.

   Momentum = _____ units

2. Multiply the mass times the velocity for the Geo Metro.

   Momentum = _____ units

3. Compare the two answers. Newton jumped in front of the car with the least momentum units. In front of which car should Newton have jumped?

Pendulums in Motion

Newton Wants You to Know

Galileo discovered the laws of the pendulum when he was only 17 years old. He was attending a religious service at the cathedral in Pisa, Italy. He noticed the chandelier was swinging back and forth. Galileo used his pulse to time the swings. He went home, set up a pendulum and discovered how a pendulum swings.

The first use of a pendulum was in clocks for accurate time measurement. Pendulums can also be used to measure the pull of gravity. Scientists call this "**g**" and give it the value of 32' (9.6 m) per second each second. Pendulums can also be used to prove that the Earth rotates. More about that later.

What Controls the Period of a Pendulum?

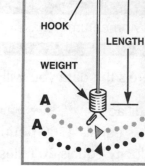

PENDULUM

HOOK

LENGTH

WEIGHT

A .... B

A ....

1. Obtain a 3' (.90 m) string.

2. Tie a weight (such as a fishing weight or big washers) to one end.

3. Tie the other end to a hook conveniently located at least 5' (1.5 m) above the ground.

Here are some facts you'll need to know.

Pendulum length is from the **bottom** of the hook to the **center** of the weight.

One complete pendulum swing is from A to B and back to A again. This is called the pendulum **period** or total time in seconds.

Now try to find out what can change the timing (or period) of a pendulum. To improve timing accuracy, obtain the total time in 10 complete swings. Divide by 10 to get the average time for one complete swing or period.

   a. Try different weights.

   b. Try different string lengths.

Name _____

c. Try different arcs. The arc is the distance from right below the pendulum to point A.

d. Try anything else you can imagine to vary the period

Complete all your experiments. What was the only thing that changed the

period of your pendulum? _____

_____

Pendulum Math

Galileo developed a formula that can predict any pendulum's period mathematically. You only need to know the pendulum's length and understand the formula to the right. The math will stretch your mind. See drawing for definitions.

Example: An 8' (2.4 m) pendulum

$$T = 2\pi \sqrt{\dfrac{L}{g}} = \text{The time it takes for one full period.}$$

$$T = 2 \times 3.14 \sqrt{\dfrac{8}{32}}$$

$$T = 2 \times 3.14 \sqrt{\dfrac{1}{4}}$$

$$T = 2 \times 3.14 \times \dfrac{1}{2}$$

T = 3.14 seconds

Try doing the pendulum math with a 32' (9.6 m) pendulum.

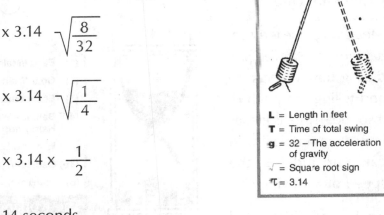

L = Length in feet
T = Time of total swing
g = 32 – The acceleration of gravity
√ = Square root sign
π = 3.14

Newton Wants You to Research

If you ever visit the United Nations Building in New York City, you will see a **Foucalt pendulum**. A Foucalt pendulum is used to prove the Earth's rotation. The pendulum in the U.N. Building has a 200-pound (90 kg) weight and a 75' (22.5 m) length.

Do some research on Foucalt pendulums. Try to explain how they work to your friends.

Name _____

Time Lab: Making Your Own Pendulum Clock

Newton Needs Time

Physicists must measure things in order to understand them. They want to know an object's length, mass and volume. In many experiments, it is equally important to measure **time**.

Measuring time is essential for space travel, predicting how objects fall and telling the pitch of a sound. Time is just as important in baking a cake or judging the speed of a moving car.

(1) **Barrel/Mainspring**
(2) **Gear Train**
(3) **Escapement**
(4) **Balance Wheel & Hairspring**
(5a) **Winding Stem**
(5b) **Oscillating Weight**
(6) **Dial Train**

The workings of a mechanical watch.

Ancient scientists used the Earth's movements to measure seasons, days and nights. The moon's trip around the Earth became the time basis for our months. Clocks were developed to measure hours and seconds. Some atomic clocks are so precise that they are only off less than one second in 300 years.

Try to imagine a life without clocks. Can you list a few problems you might have?

_____

_____

_____

_____

54

Name _____

Estimating Time

It is often useful in everyday life to estimate time *without* using a watch. Here is a way to improve your time estimation.

1. Observe how seconds change on a clock or watch.

2. Try to mentally count 30 seconds in sync with the clock.

3. Saying 1001, 1002, 1003, etc., may help you judge seconds.

4. Now try to estimate 30 seconds **without** looking at a clock.

5. Practice till you get close to estimating 30-second intervals

6. Team up with four or five students to give each other time tests. Use the Time Estimation Data Table below to organize your time estimates.

7. Have one student administer the test and record results in the data table.

8. You will be estimating 30-, 45- and 60-second time intervals.

TIME ESTIMATION DATA TABLE			
Name	**30-Second Trial**	**45-Second Trial**	**60-Second Trial**
Place an *X* if the students are within these limits.	29 to 31	43 to 47	57 to 63
1.			
2.			
3.			
4.			

Name some situations where estimating time could be useful. _____

_____

_____

Name _____

Galileo Helps You Build a Clock

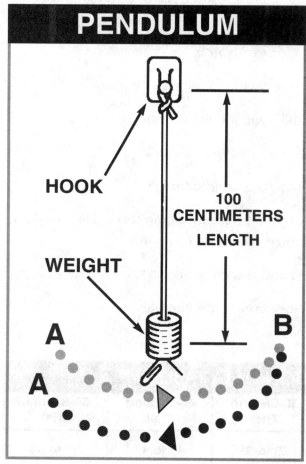

PENDULUM

HOOK

100 CENTIMETERS LENGTH

WEIGHT

A

A

B

Galileo discovered the law of the pendulum. It is used to make accurate pendulum clocks.

A pendulum with a length of 100 **centimeters** (39") has a **one second** period. That is the key to building your own pendulum clock.

1. Construct a pendulum similar to the one shown at the left using a 100-centimeter length.

Here are some facts you'll need to know.

Pendulum length is from the **bottom** of the hook to the **center** of the weight.

One complete pendulum swing is from A to B and back to A again. This is called the pendulum **period** or total time in seconds.

2. Check your pendulum's period against a watch or clock. You should get 60 periods (a swing back and forth) in 60 seconds.

3. Suppose you didn't get 60 periods in 60 seconds. Simply adjust the length of your pendulum. A shorter pendulum goes faster. A longer pendulum goes slower.

Newton Helps Explain Galileo's Pendulum: A 100-centimeter long pendulum does not exactly give a one-second period. The force of gravity affects Galileo's pendulum law. At the equator, you would need a 99.1-centimeter length. At the North Pole, you would need a 99.6-centimeter length. Gravity's force also changes from mountaintop to sea level.

The Tower of Pisa Puzzler

Newton's Pisa Puzzler Description

Newton stole this puzzler from Galileo. Galileo wondered whether heavy or light objects would fall faster. Fortunately for Galileo, he lived in Pisa, Italy. The famous Bell Tower in Pisa is 180' (54 m) high. It leans over sideways almost 15' (4.5 m).

Supposedly, Galileo stood at the base and instructed his assistants to drop light and heavy cannonballs at the same time.

Galileo died a few weeks before Newton was born. Galileo is considered the father of science experimentation. Newton learned a great deal from studying Galileo's books. From these studies and extensive experiments, Newton discovered some of the most famous laws of science.

What's the Problem?

The problem is not whether Galileo was hit by the cannonballs. He wasn't. The puzzler problem is whether the heavy or light cannonball fell faster. Of course, you will not be using cannonballs.

There are three possibilities. The heavier object could fall faster. The lighter object could fall faster. Or they could both fall at the same rate. What's your **hypothesis**

(educated guess)? _____

_____

_____

Name _____

How to Test Newton's Pisa Puzzler

1. Obtain two small stuffed animals about the same size.

2. Fill one of the stuffed animals with nails, nuts and bolts so that it is much heavier than the other.

3. **Safely** stand on a chair or table and let both go at the same time. You may have to repeat the experiment a few times to be sure of your results.

Describe what happened. _____

_____

_____

Newton Is Not Happy

Newton thinks you missed something in this Pisa Puzzler. He suggests you repeat the experiment as follows:

1. Use 51 playing cards in their card box as the heavy object.

2. Use a single playing card as the light object.

3. Stand on a chair, hold them horizontally as shown, and drop both at the same time.

4. Describe your results and explain what obviously affected the cards that didn't affect the stuffed animals. _____

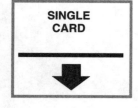

_____

_____

5. How could you drop the deck and the single card so that air resistance will not affect them? There is a simple way. Describe and try your ideas. _____

_____

_____

58

Newton's Falling Apple

How Objects Fall

Sir Isaac Newton may or may not have been hit by a falling apple. But as he experimented with falling objects, he observed that they didn't fall at a constant, steady rate. Instead, the longer they fell, the faster they went.

It will help you to understand falling objects better if you imagine yourself falling out of an airplane. The first second you only drop 16 feet (4.8 m). At the end of two seconds, you have fallen 64 feet (19.2 m). Notice that you fell 16 feet (4.8 m) the first second plus 48 feet (14.4 m) more during the next second. You are obviously speeding up. After the fifth second, you'd have gone 400 feet (120 m) which is almost the length of 1¹/₃ football fields. If you kept falling for 60 seconds, you would have traveled about 60,000 feet (18,000 m) and would have reached a speed of about 1300 miles (2093 km) per hour.

Actually, you would never reach such an enormous speed because you are falling through **air**. The air resistance would slow you up so that your final speed when you hit the ground would be very much less than 1300 miles (2093 km) per hour.

Understanding Velocity and Acceleration

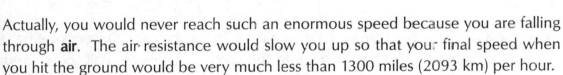

Physicists use precise definitions. Before you can go further in understanding matter in motion, you'll need some more precise definitions.

Speed. How fast an object is moving. Your dad may drive 55 miles (88.5 km) per hour. A snail may travel 2" (5 cm) per minute. In all cases, speed involves distance covered per unit of time.

Velocity. Velocity is the same as speed with one exception. Velocity is speed in a particular direction. 55 miles (88.5 km) per hour is speed. 55 miles (88.5 km) per hour going due north is velocity. Falling objects always have velocity instead of speed because they are traveling in a specific, down direction.

Name _____

Acceleration. Acceleration tells us how fast an object's velocity is changing. At a steady driving rate of 55 (88.5 km) miles per hour there is no change and therefore no acceleration. If a car speeds up to pass, then you have a velocity change and an acceleration. As you brake to stop, you again have a velocity change and a negative acceleration. Acceleration is always given in terms of velocity change per unit of time. A car might be accelerating 10 miles (16.1 km) per hour every minute.

Acceleration of Gravity—"g." The Earth's gravitational force causes a falling object to continue to speed up or accelerate. This acceleration of gravity is called "g" and is equal to about 32 feet (9.6 m) per second every second.

These definitions fit neatly into some simple formulas developed by Sir Isaac Newton to explain falling matter. Don't let them awe you. You should be able to handle them easily.

How Fast Does It Fall?

To really investigate falling objects, you should have a helicopter fly over you and drop a ball. Since that is impossible, go outside and substitute a ball thrown into the air.

1. Have a strong person throw a ball as high as he or she can. Observe the ball's motion from its highest point back to the ground. Does the ball speed up or slow down as it nears the ground?

2. Again have a strong person throw the ball as high as they can. Use a stopwatch to find out how many seconds it took to fall from its highest point back to the ground. You may have to repeat the experiment a few times. How many seconds did it take for the ball to fall to the ground from its highest point? _____ seconds

You know how many seconds it took for the ball to fall back to Earth. Here is the math formula you need to compute your ball's velocity when it struck the Earth.

VELOCITY = ACCELERATION of GRAVITY multiplied by TIME

$V = g \times T$

> **Example:** Assume your ball took five seconds to fall.
>
> $V = g \times T$
>
> $V = 32 \times 5$
>
> $V = 160$ feet (48 m) per second

V = Velocity in feet (meters) per second

g = Acceleration of gravity which is 32 feet (9.6 m) per second each second

T = Time of falling in seconds

60

Name _____

Now place your falling ball time in the formula and find its final velocity.

V = 32 x _____ = _____ feet (meters) per second

Assuming no air resistance, find the final velocity in each case below.

An object falling for 8 seconds. _____ feet (meters) per second

An object falling for 12 seconds. _____ feet (meters) per second

An object falling for 25 seconds. _____ feet (meters) per second

How Far Did It Fall?

$$D = \frac{gT^2}{2}$$

D = Distance in feet

g = 32 (the acceleration of gravity)

T = Time

T² = Time multiplied by itself

Example: Assume an object fell for 10 seconds.

$$D = \frac{gT^2}{2}$$

$$D = \frac{32 \times 10 \times 10}{2}$$

$$D = \frac{3200}{2}$$

D = 1600 feet

Go back to page 60 and find the time it took for your ball to fall back to Earth. Place that time into Newton's distance formula and find out the distance it fell.

Falling ball distance = _____ feet (meters)

Assume an object fell for 8 seconds. How far did it fall? _____ feet (meters)

Assume an object fell for 12 seconds. How far did it fall? _____ feet (meters)

Assume an object fell for 30 seconds. How far did it fall? _____ feet (meters)

FALLING OBJECT DATA TABLE		
Time (seconds)	**Distance** (feet)	**Velocity** (feet per second)
0	0	0
1	16	32
2	64	64
3	144	96
4	256	128
5	400	160

Physical Science 23

NEWTON'S ACTION LAB

Falling Fun

Gravity Accelerates Everywhere

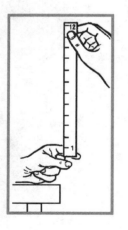

Gravity pulls everything down. Drop a ball and it returns to Earth. A feather separated from a bird eventually floats down. Even a speeding bullet obeys gravity and falls to Earth.

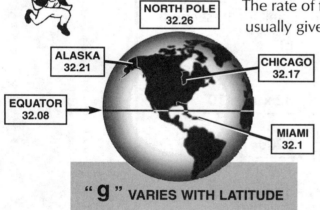

NORTH POLE 32.26

ALASKA 32.21

CHICAGO 32.17

EQUATOR 32.08

MIAMI 32.1

" g " VARIES WITH LATITUDE

The rate of falling is determined by the **acceleration of gravity**. This is usually given as "g" and is equal to 32 feet (9.6 m) per second every second. Acceleration causes a falling body to speed up as it falls. You are falling much more rapidly after three seconds than you are after the first second.

The acceleration of gravity is not the same everywhere on Earth. Gravity pulls you less at the equator than at the North Pole. A person weighing 150 pounds (67.5 kg) at the equator would actually weigh 150½ pounds (67.7 kg) at the North Pole. The diagram on the left shows how "**g**" varies with latitude.

Catch a Falling Ruler

In this activity your reaction time will be competing against the acceleration of gravity. It will be your brains and muscles trying to beat the Earth's "g."

1. Obtain a ruler. Place your hand on a table so that your thumb and index finger extend over the table.

2. Have a friend hold the zero end of the ruler between your thumb and index finger.

3. Without warning, your friend will drop the ruler. Use your thumb and index finger to grab the falling ruler.

4. Try the ruler drop three times and record your best catch (lowest inches [centimeters]). _____ Your best catch in inches (centimeters).

Here's a scale to rate your reaction time.		
0"-2" (0-5 cm)	☞	You are cheating.
2"-4" (5-10 cm)	☞	Excellent
4"-6" (10-15 cm)	☞	Good
6"-8" (15-20 cm)	☞	Fair
8"-12" (20-30 cm)	☞	You need help.

Name _____

Try four other people. Give them three tries and record their best catch.

1. _____   2. _____

3. _____   4. _____

Newton wants you to have a better idea of how fast the ruler drops. He has converted the inches into falling time. Study the chart below. What was the falling time for your best catch?

_____ time in seconds

DISTANCE RULER FELL IN INCHES	2	3	4	5	6	7	8	9	10	11	12
TIME OF FALL IN SECONDS	0.1	0.13	0.14	0.16	0.18	0.19	0.20	0.22	0.23	0.24	0.25

Newton's Falling Puzzler

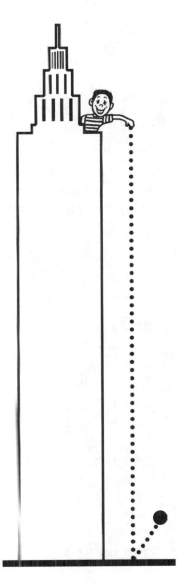

The Empire State Building is in New York City. It has 102 floors and is 1250 feet (375 m) tall.

Suppose you dropped a ball from the very top of the Empire State Building. Assume there is no wind. The ball would land 5" (13 cm) east of the true vertical. True vertical is the point directly below the ball when it was released.

Try to explain why the ball was 5" (13 cm) off true vertical. Use the space below.

_____

_____

_____

_____

_____

Answer Key

Circular Math, page 7

You will need to place the number one in the center circle.

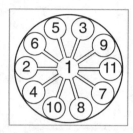

A Quick Review of Matter, page 9

1. mass
2. space
3. matter
4. grams, kilograms
5. gravity
6. scale
7. changes

Atomic Animals, page 31

Seal = Selenium + Aluminum

Bear = Beryllium + Argon

Cow = Carbon + Oxygen + Tungsten

Snakes = Sulfur + Sodium + Potassium + Einsteinium

Shark = Sulfur + Hydrogen + Argon + Potassium

Rhinoceros = Rhodium + Indium + Oxygen +
 Cerium + Radon + Oxygen + Sulfur

Puzzling Atoms, page 33

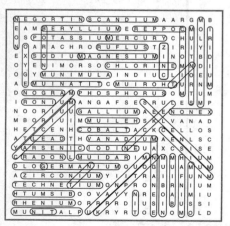

Newton's Action Reaction Puzzler, page 46

The cork will first move forward in the direction of the shove. This may seem contrary to what you experience when a car suddenly moves forward. The law involved here is Newton's Law of Action and Reaction. The law states that for every action, there is an equal and opposite reaction. As you push the jar forward, the water obeys Newton's law and moves backward. The floating cork is acted upon by the water moving backward. The cork also obeys Newton's law by moving in the opposite direction to the moving water. Therefore, it initially moves forward.

Newton's Puzzler Description, page 50

Jump in front of the Cadillac. It has only 90,000 momentum units. The fast moving Geo has 119,000 momentum units. Better still, be a live coward and stick with the helicopter.

Newton Is Not Happy, page 58

Both the heavy and the light stuffed animals will appear to fall at the same rate. The pull of gravity accelerates heavy and light objects equally. The statement above is only true if you ignore the effects of air resistance. In a vacuum, a feather and a bowling ball will fall at the same rate. The single card fell slower than the deck of cards because of the air resistance. Place the single card on **top** of the deck of cards and drop them. They will fall at the same rate because the deck breaks the air resistance for the single card.

Newton's Falling Puzzler, page 63

During the time it took the ball to drop, the Earth rotated slightly.